SEPUP
Issue-Oriented Science

ISSUES AND
PHYSICAL SCIENCE

Waves

THIRD EDITION
REVISED FOR NGSS

SEPUP
Issue-Oriented Science

ISSUES AND
PHYSICAL SCIENCE

Waves

THIRD EDITION
REVISED FOR NGSS

THE LAWRENCE HALL OF SCIENCE
UNIVERSITY OF CALIFORNIA, BERKELEY

This book is part of SEPUP's middle school science course sequence. For more information about this sequence, see the SEPUP and Lab-Aids websites.

ISSUES AND EARTH SCIENCE

ISSUES AND LIFE SCIENCE

ISSUES AND PHYSICAL SCIENCE

Additional SEPUP instructional materials include:
SEPUP Modules: Grades 7–12
Science and Sustainability: Course for Grades 9–12
Science and Global Issues: Biology: Course for High School Biology

This material is based upon work supported by the National Science Foundation under Grants No. 9252906 and No. 0099265. Any opinions, findings, and conclusions or recommendations expressed in this material are those of the authors and do not necessarily reflect the views of the National Science Foundation.

The preferred citation format for this book is SEPUP. (2017). *Issues and Physical Science: Waves.* Lawrence Hall of Science, University of California at Berkeley. Published by Lab-Aids®, Inc., Ronkonkoma, NY

Third Edition

Q1 2 3 4 5 6 7 8 9   20 19 18 17 16

ISBN: 978-1-63093-418-7
ISBN: 1-63093-418-6

SEPUP
Lawrence Hall of Science
University of California at Berkeley
Berkeley CA 94720-5200

e-mail: sepup@berkeley.edu
Website: www.sepuplhs.org

Published by:

Lab-aids®

17 Colt Court
Ronkonkoma NY 11779
Website: www.lab-aids.com

A Letter to *Issues and Physical Science* Students

As you examine the activities in this book, you may wonder, "Why does this book look so different from other science books I've seen?" The reason is simple: it is a different kind of science program, and only some of what you will learn can be seen by leafing through this book!

Issues and Physical Science uses several kinds of activities to teach science. As you conduct these activities, you will engage in the same practices used by scientists to understand the natural world and by engineers to solve problems. For example, you will observe and test the properties of elements and compounds. You will model the atoms and molecules that make up these substances. You will plan and carry out investigations to explore energy transfer, and the properties of waves. You will investigate the motion of a cart on a ramp, and apply what you learn to the physics of automobile accidents and safety features. A combination of laboratories, investigations, readings, models, scientific debates, role plays, and projects will help you develop your understanding of science and the relevance of physical science to your interests.

You will find that important scientific ideas come up again and again in different activities throughout the program. You will be expected to do more than just memorize these concepts: you will be asked to develop explanations and apply them to solve problems. In particular, you will improve your decision-making skills by using evidence to weigh outcomes and to decide what you think should be done about the scientific issues facing our society.

How do we know that this is a good way for you to learn? In general, research on science education supports it. In particular, many of the activities in this book were tested by hundreds of students and their teachers, and then modified on the basis of their feedback. New activities are based on what we learned in classrooms using the materials and on new research on science learning. In a sense, this entire book is the result of an investigation: we had people test our ideas, we interpreted the results, and we then revised our ideas! We believe the result will show you that learning more about science is important, enjoyable, and relevant to your life.

SEPUP Staff

ISSUES & PHYSICAL SCIENCE THIRD EDITION

Director: Barbara Nagle

Co-Director: John Howarth

Coordinator: Janet Bellantoni

AUTHORS

Waves: Janet Bellantoni, John Howarth, and Christopher Keller

OTHER CONTRIBUTORS

Timothy Hurt, Barbara Nagle, Maia Willcox

CONTENT AND SCIENTIFIC REVIEW

Dr. Bernhard Beck-Winchatz, DePaul University

Dr. Stephanie Chasteen, University of Colorado, Boulder

Dr. Noah Podolefsky, University of Colorado, Boulder

PRODUCTION

Coordination, Design, Photo Research, Composition: Seventeenth Street Studios

Editing: Kerry Oullet

FIELD TEST CENTERS

Issues and Physical Science is a revision of *Issues, Evidence, and You* (IEY). We are extremely grateful to the center directors and teachers who taught the original and revised program. These teachers and their students contributed significantly to improving the course. Since then, *Issues and Physical Science* has been used in many classrooms across the United States. This third edition is based on what we have learned from teachers and students in those classrooms. It also includes new data and information, so the issues included in the course remain fresh and up-to-date.

IEY CENTERS

Alaska: Donna York (Director), Kim Bunselmeyer, Linda Churchill, James Cunningham, Patty Dietderich, Lori Gilliam, Gina Ireland-Kelly, Mary Klopfer, Jim Petrash, Amy Spargo

California-San Bernardino County: Dr. Herbert Brunkhorst (Director), William Cross, Alan Jolliff, Kimberly Michael, Chuck Schindler

California-San Diego County: Mike Reeske and Marilyn Stevens (Co-Directors), Pete Brehm, Donna Markey, Susan Mills, Barney Preston, Samantha Swann

California-San Francisco Area: Stephen Rutherford (Director), Michael Delnista, Cindy Donley, Judith Donovan, Roger Hansen, Judi Hazen, Catherine Heck, Mary Beth Hodge, Mary Hoglund, Mary Pat Horn, Paul Hynds, Margaret Kennedy, Carol Mortensen, Bob Rosenfeld, Jan Vespi

Colorado: John E. Sepich (Director), Mary Ann Hart, Lisa Joss, Geree Pepping-Dremel, Tracy Schuster, Dan Stebbins, Terry Strahm

Connecticut: Dave Lopath (Director), Harald Bender, Laura Boehm, Antonella Bona-Gallo, Joseph Bosco, Timothy Dillon, Victoria Duers, Valerie Hoye, Bob Segal, Stephen Weinberg

Kentucky-Lexington Area: Dr. Stephen Henderson and Susie Nally (Co-Directors), Stephen Dilly, Ralph McKee II, Barry Welty, Laura Wright

Kentucky-Louisville Area: Ken Rosenbaum (Director), Ella Barrickman, Pamela T. Boykin, Bernis Crawford, Cynthia Detwiler, Denise Finley, Ellen Skomsky

Louisiana: Dr. Shiela Pirkle (Director), Kathy McWaters, Lori Ann Otts, Robert Pfrimmer, Eileen Shieber, Mary Ann Smith, Allen (Bob) Toups, Dorothy Trusclair

Michigan: Phillip Larsen, Dawn Pickard and Peter Vunovich (Co-Directors), Ann Aho, Carolyn Delia, Connie Duncan, Kathy Grosso, Stanley Guzy, Kevin Kruger, Tommy Ragonese

New York City: Arthur Camins (Director), Eddie Bennett, Steve Chambers, Sheila Cooper, Sally Dyson

North Carolina: Dr. Stan Hill and Dick Shaw (Co-Directors), Kevin Barnard, Ellen Dorsett, Cameron Holbrook, Anne M. Little

Oklahoma: Shelley Fisher (Director), Jill Anderson, Nancy Bauman, Larry Joe Bradford, Mike Bynum, James Granger, Brian Lomenick, Belva Nichols, Linda Sherrill, Keith Symcox, David Watson

Pennsylvania: Dr. John Agar (Director), Charles Brendley, Gregory France, John Frederick, Alana Gazetski, Gill Godwin

Washington, D.C.: Frances Brock and Alma Miller (Co-Directors), Vasanti Alsi, Yvonne Brannum, Walter Bryant, Shirley DeLaney, Sandra Jenkins, Joe Price, John Spearman

Western New York: Dr. Robert Horvat and Dr. Joyce Swartney (Co-Directors), Rich Bleyle, Kathaleen Burke, Al Crato, Richard Duquin, Lillian Gondree, Ray Greene, Richard Leggio, David McClatchey, James Morgan, Susan Wade

Contents

Waves

Waves

GEMMA LOOKED OUTSIDE. *After days of rainy weather, it was finally a bright and sunny day. "Mom, I am heading outside to meet Sam," Gemma called to her mother. She grabbed her headphones and headed for the door.*

"Remember your sunglasses!" said her mother. Gemma swept them off the kitchen counter as she left and put them on. Listening to her music, she walked down the street and joined her friend Samantha at the corner.

"Hey," said Sam, pointing at Gemma's sunglasses. "My glasses are just like those. Only blue."

Gemma took out her headphones to be able to hear to her friend. "Well, why aren't you wearing them?"

"Oh, I don't like wearing them. They bother my nose," Sam said.

"My mom says the sun can damage your eyes. Have you ever heard of that? We have a lot of bright days around here, so maybe you should wear them," Gemma said with concern.

"Yeah, you're probably right. But aren't you worried about hurting your ears with those headphones turned up so loud?" said Sam with equal concern for her friend.

• • •

What are the properties of the waves and how do waves transmit sound and light energy? How are sound and light waves similar and different? What happens when waves move from air to another material, such as water, a mirror, or cloth? When are waves harmful? How do scientists and engineers use waves for research and communication?

To investigate these questions, you will use mathematics to recognize patterns in the properties of waves. You will use models to compare the properties of various waves and communicate explanations about them. You will integrate scientific and technical information as you investigate advances in communication technologies.

1 It's A Noisy World

INVESTIGATION

JOSÉ AND JENNA *were talking at lunch. The cafeteria was noisy, though, and José was having a hard time understanding Jenna. Jenna thought it was weird that he wasn't able to hear her very well. Later they talked in a quieter place.*

"José, I'm a little worried about your hearing," Jenna said.

"What do you mean?" José asked.

"Well, I noticed that sometimes you don't hear me call to you. I have to repeat myself."

"Well, actually, sometimes I don't hear my teacher right. Yesterday I didn't know what she said in class and I ended up doing the wrong thing."

"You should get your hearing tested."

"I've had it tested before, and it was fine. I don't see why it would change."

There are a number of causes of hearing loss. It can be present at birth or develop later in life. Some people are genetically more likely to lose their hearing, although it is not yet known which people are at higher risk. Occupational noises, recreational noises, some medications, and illnesses can all cause hearing loss.

Sound intensity is a measurement of how much sound energy passes through a certain area in a certain amount of time as it spreads out from the source. Scientists measure sound intensity in watts per square meter (W/m^2). A common way of describing sound is with the decibel scale. The **decibel** (dB) is a unit of measure that indicates the relative intensity of a sound. In this activity, you will investigate the decibel scale and how the human ear responds to various levels of intensity.

GUIDING QUESTION

What is the range of sound intensities that humans can hear?

MATERIALS

For each pair of students

    1 set of 5 Sound cards

PROCEDURE

1. With your partner, examine the Sound cards. Each card represents a particular sound. The number of shaded squares on the card represents the intensity of sound and its decibel level.

2. Make a data table similar to the one below.

Comparing the Intensity of Certain Sounds					
Card	Type of sound	Number of squares shaded	Total number of squares on card	Proportion of shaded squares on card	Sound Measurement
A					
B					
C					
D					
E					

3. Based on the data for each card, complete the table.

4. With your partner, examine the data in the table and look for a relationship between the change in the number of shaded squares and the change in decibel level. Record your findings in your science notebook.

5. The table below shows the sound levels of some common sounds. In your science notebook, copy the first two columns of the table. Complete the second column of the table. Do this by using the relationship you determined in Step 4 to calculate how many times more intense each sound is compared to a whisper.

Sound Levels of Common Noises		
Decibels	*Relative Intensity*	*Noise source*
Safe range		
0	*1*	*Threshold of hearing*
10		*Breathing*
20		*Whisper, rustling leaves*
30		*Quiet bedroom, park*
40		*Quiet library*
50		*Average home or office*
60		*Normal conversation, 1 m away; clothes dryer*
70		*Vacuum cleaner, 1 m away; average road noise, 25 m away; inside car; headphone use in quiet environment*
Risky range		
80		*Heavy city traffic, at curb; power lawn mower; hair dryer; freight train @ 40 km/h; noisy restaurant; headphone use in most outdoor places*
90		*Diesel truck, 1 m away; average factory floor*
100		*Snowmobile, 15th row of rock concert, circular saw, typical musical instrument*
110		*Chain saw, 1 m away; leaf blower*
Injury range		
120		*Ambulance siren, jackhammer, car horn, front row of rock concert or symphony, max headphone level*
130		*Threshold of pain*
140		*Jet engine, 50 m away; firecracker; gunshot*
Instant perforation of eardrum		
160		*Some explosions*

6. A **pattern** is something that happens in a repeated and predict-able way. What patterns did you find in the data table above?

7. Use the table and data from the Sound cards to calculate how many times more intense a noise at the threshold of pain is than a whisper. Discuss with your partner the range of intensities that the human ear can hear.

ANALYSIS

1. What is the range of sound intensities that humans can hear, from the quietest sound to one that causes pain?

2. What is the advantage of using the decibel scale to indicate intensity of sound?

3. If a sound increases by 10 dB, how many times more intense is the sound?

4. A set of noise-reducing headphones will reduce the relative intensity of a noise by 100 times.
   a. If these headphones are used while operating a leaf blower, will the noise be reduced to a safe range?
   b. How much of a reduction in relative intensity is needed for the headphones to further reduce the sound to a whisper?
   c. Use ratios to explain your reasoning for item 4b.

5. Most people perceive an increase of 10 dB as a doubling in volume of a sound.
   a. How many times louder is a 70-dB sound than a 40-dB sound? Explain how you used the information about the relationship between decibels and volume to determine your answer.
   b. How much more intense is a 70-dB sound than a 40-dB sound? Explain the concepts you used and how you used them to determine your answer.

6. **Reflection:** What sounds do you and/or your family encounter regularly that could potentially harm your hearing?

2 Making Sound Waves

INVESTIGATION

José made an appointment with his doctor, who referred him to a hearing center. At the center, an audiologist examined José and conducted a hearing test. She asked José to wear headphones and then played numerous tones with varying loudness levels to one ear at a time. The audiologist changed the sound and recorded whether José could hear it or not. She repeated the tests several times for each ear.

Hearing loss does not necessarily mean a person hears all types of sound less clearly. The results of José's hearing tests indicated that his hearing was fine for some pitches, but not all. A sound's pitch is closely related to its **frequency**, or the number of vibrations per second the ear receives. High-frequency sounds, like those produced by a flute, have a higher pitch, while low-frequency sounds, such as those produced by a tuba, have a lower pitch. Frequencies for waves are measured in **hertz** (Hz), or wave cycles per second. In this activity, you will investigate sounds of varying frequencies and intensities.

An **audiogram** is a graph that shows the sensitivity of a person's hearing for various frequencies. José's test results showed that his hearing was most affected in the range higher than 3,000 Hz. This means José could have difficulty distinguishing female speech in a noisy environment.

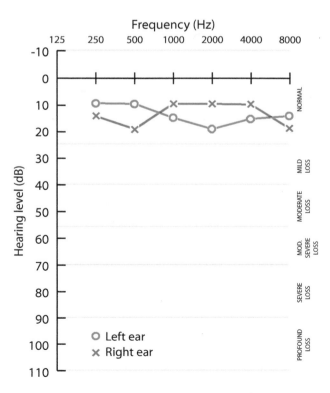

An audiogram for someone with normal hearing

GUIDING QUESTION

How can we model sound waves?

MATERIALS

Part A
For the class

       cardstock paper or cardboard

       toothed wheels on spindles (axles)

       sound tubes

       selection of musical instruments

Part B
For each group of four students

    1 long metal spring

For each student

    1 pair of safety goggles

PROCEDURE

Part A

1. Examine the items that your teacher has provided for the class.

2. In your group of four, choose an item (or combination of items) and try to make sounds.

3. For the item, carefully look at its **structure,** or the way something is formed, built, or organized. Discuss with your group how its structure contributes to its function. **Function** is a purpose for which a particular thing is used. Record your findings in your science notebook.

4. Use the item to make the sound. In your science notebook, list the sound and describe how it was made.

5. Try to make the sound louder or softer. Record what you did to make the sound louder or softer.

6. Try to make the pitch of the sound higher or lower. Record what you did to make the pitch higher or lower.

7. Repeat Steps 2–6 for a different item.

8. In your group, discuss any patterns that you noticed between the different items when making (a) louder sounds and (b) higher pitch sounds.

Part B

9. The diagram below shows a model of a sound wave traveling through air in a tube. In some parts of the wave, the air molecules are squeezed together. These areas are called **compressions**. Compressions are regions of high air pressure. Between each compression, there are areas where the air molecules are spread out. These are called **rarefactions**. Rarefactions are regions of low air pressure.

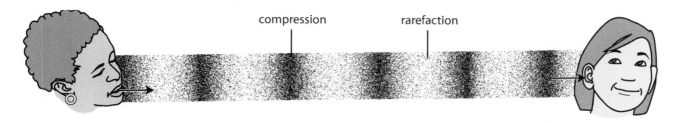

   In your group of four, use the diagram above and the long spring to create a model of a sound wave that moves through air. Use the coils of the spring to represent groups of air molecules.

10. Adjust the long spring to model a louder sound.

    Hint: Refer to the patterns that you noticed in Part A.

11. Adjust the long spring to model a higher frequency.

12. Discuss with your group how to model a sound wave of high or low intensity. Adjust the long spring to model a high-intensity sound.

ANALYSIS

1. A **wave** is a disturbance that repeats regularly in space and time and that transmits energy from one place to another with no transfer of matter. Do the sounds discussed in this activity fit the definition of a wave? Explain, using an example from this activity.

2. Predict what happens to the amount of energy transmitted by a wave if
   a. the frequency is increased.
   b. the loudness is reduced.

3. Sound is known as a *pressure wave*. Did your model support this claim? Explain how it did or did not.

4. Make two tables like the one below, and fill in the missing diagrams to show changes in loudness and frequency. Then explain what your diagrams model.

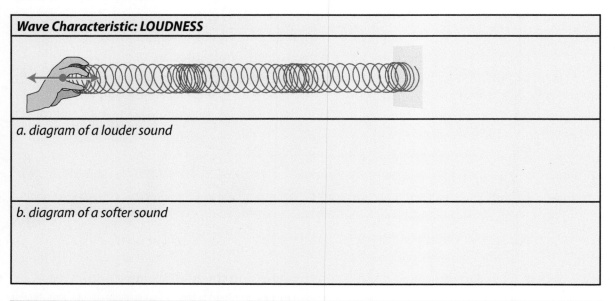

Wave Characteristic: LOUDNESS
a. diagram of a louder sound
b. diagram of a softer sound

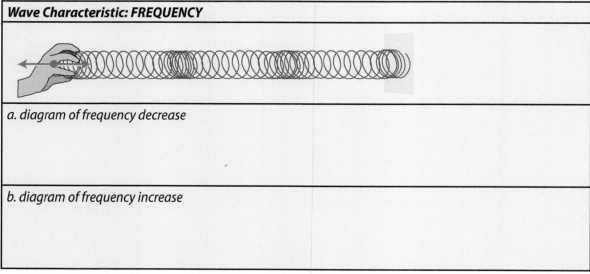

Wave Characteristic: FREQUENCY
a. diagram of frequency decrease
b. diagram of frequency increase

5. Match the following descriptions of people to their audiograms:

   a: José has decreased hearing in the right ear at higher frequencies.

   b: Leon has noticed lately that he has trouble deciphering women's speech.

   c: Shannon has moderate hearing loss involving sounds of 3,000–6,000 Hz.

   d: Sophia has severe to profound hearing loss in both ears.

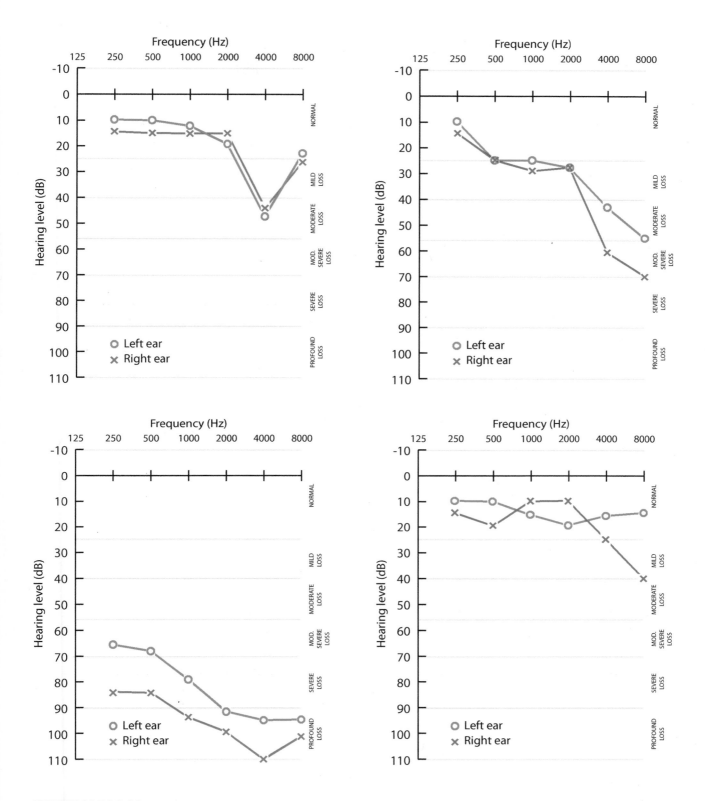

EXTENSION

What is *perfect pitch* and how does it relate to the frequency of a sound?
Investigate which individuals are more likely to have perfect pitch.

3 *The Nature Of Sound*

READING

THE VARIATION OF sounds in the world is vast. Some sound waves carry small amounts of energy, such as a whisper or the sound of breathing. Other waves, such as the sound from an explosion, can be loud enough to damage tissue in the ear. Some sounds, such as voice or music, carry complex information. Despite the wide variety of sounds, all types of waves share some of the same characteristics, such as frequency and speed. In this activity, you will read about these common characteristics that identify sound. Then you will explore ways that sound is used in everyday devices.

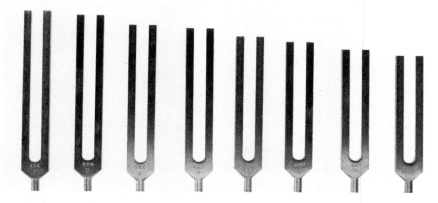

Tuning forks of various frequencies

GUIDING QUESTION

What are the properties of sound waves?

READING

Longitudinal Waves

Sound waves, like some other mechanical waves, are longitudinal waves. A **longitudinal wave** is one that transfers energy through compressions and rarefactions in the material through which the energy travels. A compression is the region of the wave in which the material through which the wave is transmitted is pressed together. A rarefaction is the region in which the material is spread apart. When you hear a sound wave through the air, you are detecting a disturbance in the pressure of the air. In a longitudinal wave, like sound, the material in which the energy travels vibrates parallel to the direction the energy travels.

Direction of particle motion in medium   Direction of wave transmission

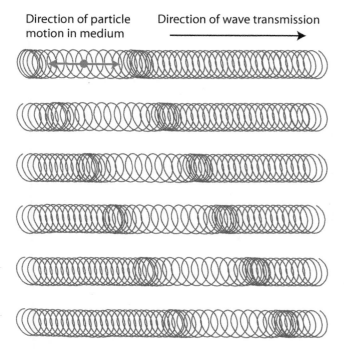

Wave Media

When a wave transmits energy, it is important to note that the individual molecules or particles in the medium are not transmitted. In other words, the medium does not move along with the wave. A **medium** (plural is media) is the material in which wave energy travels. Mechanical waves, such as sound or seismic waves, move through the ground, water, air, and other materials. For example, when making varied noises with rubber bands in a previous activity, the rubber band vibrating was the source of the wave, but the medium was air through which the energy travelled. The disturbance moved away from the source through a medium to our ears. When this happened, the air did not permanently change its position relative to the source. Namely, the air touching the rubber band did not move across the room and land in someone's ear. The medium itself—the air—was not transferred from the source of the sound to the receiver of the energy.

Speed of Sound

The **speed of sound** can be directly measured, like moving objects, using the relationship

$$speed = \frac{distance}{time}$$

For example, the sound from a thunderclap that happens 1,000 m away and takes 2.9 s to get to you, traveled at an average speed of

$$speed = \frac{1,000\ m}{2.9\ s}$$
$$= 345\ m/s$$

Waves travel at various speeds depending on the medium. The same wave travels at different speeds through different substances. The speed is affected by physical properties, such as the density of the material. For example, sound travels about 10 times faster through wood than through air, as shown in the table on the next page. The tight spacing of the vibrating molecules in the denser material enables sound to travel faster. In general, but not always, sound travels faster through solids than liquids and faster through liquids than gases.

Sound also travels at various speeds through the same substance depending on its temperature and humidity (if it is a gas). For example, sound travels faster in hot air compared with cooler air

A supersonic jet traveling faster than the speed of sound. The vapor cone behind the jet is a cloud of condensed water that forms due to humid air entering a low-pressure region. This phenomenon also occurs with slower moving aircraft, such as the two white trails observed behind planes approaching an airport.

because the air molecules are moving quicker, which increases the speed at which they transfer energy. The speed of sound in air changes from 331 m/s at 0° C to 355 m/s at 40° C.

Because sound waves depend on the physical disturbance of atoms or molecules, they must have a medium in order to travel. Sound cannot transmit energy through a vacuum because there are no atoms or molecules in a vacuum. Although outer space is not a perfect vacuum, the molecules are so far apart that they do not allow for compressions and rarefactions. Therefore, sound cannot travel in outer space.

Speed of Sound

Medium	Speed (m/s)
Vacuum	0
Carbon dioxide (0°C)	258
Air (20°C)	344
Helium (20°C)	927
Water, fresh (20°C)	1,481
Wood	3,500
Aluminum	6,400

STOP TO THINK 2

What is the speed of sound for a noise that travels 2 km in 5.8 s?

Sound and Hearing

Hearing is a result of a sound wave transmitting from the air though the various parts of the ear, from the outer to the inner ear where the signal is sent to the brain for interpretation. When a sound wave reaches the ear, the compressions and rarefactions are first channeled through the outer ear onto the eardrum, or the tympanic membrane. The vibration on this flexible membrane is transmitted into the middle ear. Once in the middle ear, the vibration is transmitted quickly through an opening (known as the oval window) in three small solid bones to another membrane on the inner side of the middle ear. This vibration sends energy into the inner ear. The inner ear contains the cochlea, a snail-shaped organ filled with fluid. When the vibration from the oval window moves the fluid in the cochlea, the fluid activates up to 25,000 tiny specialized cells. The specialized cells, called cilia, then send an electrical signal to the brain through the auditory nerve.

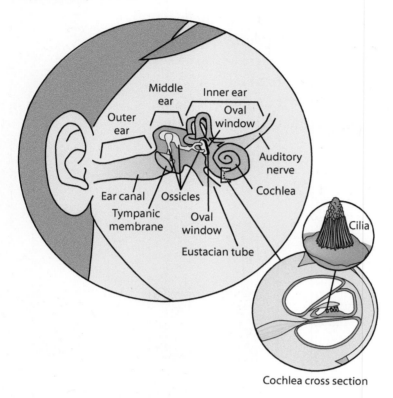

Cochlea cross section

A person's hearing loss depends on which parts of the ear do not respond to these waves. Problems with the outer or middle ear lead to inefficient transfer of sound. This type of hearing loss is called *conductive hearing loss* because the outer and middle ear do not conduct the sound into the inner ear. Conductive hearing loss can be caused by things such as a hole in the eardrum, inflammation of the middle ear, excessive wax, trauma to the head, or dysfunctional bones in the middle ear. *Sensorineural hearing loss* means that sound arrives to the inner ear, but the information is not fully passed on to the auditory nerve. For example, repetitive exposure to a sound at the same frequency will damage the cilia cells that receive that particular frequency such that they can no longer respond to that frequency.

Sensorineural hearing loss can be inherited or caused by things such as old age, a sudden loud noise, repeated exposure, medication, inner ear infection, or head trauma. It is possible for a person to have both conductive and sensorineural hearing loss, which is known as *mixed hearing loss*.

STOP TO THINK 3

If you have an ear infection that temporarily adds fluid to the middle ear, what kind of hearing loss do you have?

Wave Energy and Amplitude

For sound and other mechanical waves, the amount of wave energy is related to its amplitude. The **amplitude** of a wave is the maximum displacement from its state of rest. For sound, amplitude is closely related to the sound's intensity, which was explored in previous activities. It can be measured as a distance or a pressure. The units for amplitude vary depending on the kind of wave.

Amplitude Comparison

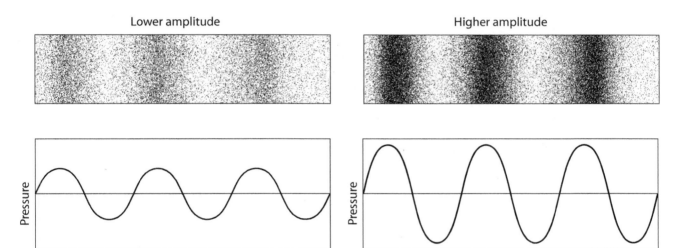

These diagrams model sound. The top row uses dots to represent air molecules and the bottom row shows variation of air pressure. The waves on the right have higher amplitude than those on the left.

If two waves are traveling at the same speed and frequency, the one with the larger amplitude will deliver more energy. For example, if water waves are hitting the shore, a taller wave will hit the shore with more energy. Likewise, a sound wave with a bigger amplitude will sound louder. The relationship between the amplitude and the energy of a wave is shown in the graph on the next page.

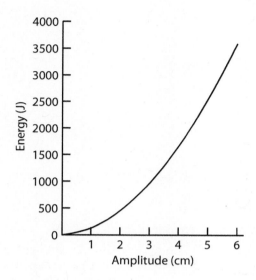

Another way to increase the amount of energy transferred over time by a wave is to increase the frequency. Increasing the frequency of a wave will deliver more cycles of energy in a given amount of time. For example, if water waves are hitting the shore and the frequency is doubled, then twice as many waves will hit the shore. If the energy of each wave is the same, then twice as much energy is delivered. In sound, a higher frequency at the same amplitude delivers more energy into the ear.

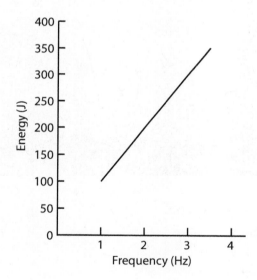

STOP TO THINK 4

What are two ways to increase the energy of a wave?

Extending the Senses

Since our world is full of the sights and sounds of waves, scientists and engineers have created many devices to help us better understand the waves around us. One critical invention is the hearing aid, which contains a small microprocessor that clarifies and amplifies sound for an individual.

Another everyday device that allows us to extend our senses is sonar. Sonar uses sound produced at frequencies that are not detectable by human ears. Sonar allows personnel on ships and submarines to detect the depth of water and the presence of fish and other boats on or under the surface. It does so by bouncing sound waves off the surfaces and calculating distances based on the time taken for the echo to return to the device.

Some animals, such as the bat and dolphin shown here, navigate their environments using sound waves.

Another important device related to sound waves is the seismograph. This device detects longitudinal waves in the earth in the form of seismic waves. Seismic waves are low-frequency waves caused by such events as explosions and earthquakes. By measuring seismic waves with a seismograph—even those waves that are not felt by humans on Earth's surface—scientists locate earthquake epicenters

and create maps showing regions at risk of
earthquakes. All of these examples illustrate ways
in which people have invented devices that use
wave energy to measure things we would not
ordinarily see or hear.

Seismograph

STOP TO THINK 5

What is another example of a device that uses sound waves?

ANALYSIS

1. If you started the motor of a boat in the middle of a lake, who
   would detect the sound of the motor first: a friend sitting on the
   shore of the lake or a friend snorkeling just below the surface
   of the water at the same distance from the boat? Explain your
   answer.

2. Lightning and thunder occur at the same time, yet we see the
   flash of lightning before we hear the clap of thunder. What does
   this indicate about the speed of light compared with the speed of
   sound?

3. Whales communicate with other whales by making low-frequency
   sounds. They navigate by making high-frequency sounds that
   echo back to them. Military sonar systems on ships produce
   sounds as loud as 200 dB, and these sounds travel great distances
   across oceans. Describe how such systems might affect whales.

4. Look at the following graphs that show the relationship between
   the amplitude and energy for a wave. Which one was supported
   by the patterns you observed in the reading?

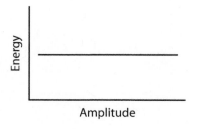

Graph A

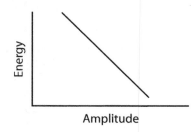

Graph B

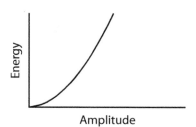

Graph C

5. If you want to increase the amount of energy a wave transfers over time, will it be most effective to double the frequency or double the amplitude? Explain using the graphs in the Reading and provide an example.

6. A student stands 100 m in front of a large smooth wall and claps loudly. Another student figures out the time for the sound to travel to the wall and back. If the sound takes 0.58 s for the sound to leave and return, what is the speed of the sound?

EXTENSION

Find through research an example of a technology not found in the Reading that uses sound to extend the way we measure, explore, model, and compute during scientific investigation. Explain how the technology uses sound.

4 Noise-Induced Hearing Loss

INVESTIGATION

NOISE-INDUCED HEARING LOSS (NIHL) occurs when sounds damage hearing, either temporarily or permanently. Harmful noises are sounds that are too loud or loud sounds that last a long time. Long-term exposure to loud noises causes permanent hearing loss by damaging sensitive cells in the inner ear. Once damaged, these cells send an incomplete electrical message to the brain, which results in sensorineural hearing loss.

Exposure to excessive noise is the most frequently avoidable cause of permanent hearing loss. This exposure puts people at **risk**, which is the chance that an action or event could result in something unfavorable happening, such as injury. People at risk for NIHL are those who are exposed to loud sounds regularly, such as firemen, musicians, truck drivers, and headphone users. People exposed to a sudden burst of noise may suffer hearing loss, but NIHL more commonly occurs gradually from long-term noise exposure. People at risk for damage can prevent permanent damage with a few simple strategies. Unfortunately, most people are not aware of the degree of risk.

GUIDING QUESTION

What can be done to prevent noise-induced hearing loss?

More than 22 million workers are exposed to potentially dangerous noises each year.

MATERIALS

For each student

    1 sheet of graph paper

PROCEDURE

Part A: How Much Is Too Much?

1. Review the intensity table, "Sound Levels of Common Noises," provided in Activity 1, "It's a Noisy World." Compare those data to the table below, "Federal Noise Standards," which shows the maximum job-related noise exposure for unprotected ears allowed by federal regulation.

Federal Noise Standards

Sound Level, Decibels	Typical Activities	Maximum Allowed Job-Noise Exposure, Daily Duration
90	Typical factory work	8 h
95	Driving a subway, tractor	4 h
100	High-volume headphone use; playing musical instrument; power boating; riding snow mobile, motorcycle	2 h
105	Sporting events, mowing the lawn	1 h
110	Dancing at a club; playing drums; using power tools, chain saw	30 min
115	Front-row rock concert, cheering stadium crowd	15 min or less

U.S. Dept. of Labor, Occupational Safety and Health Administration (OSHA)

2. Plot a line graph of daily duration (y-axis) vs. sound level (x-axis). Label the graph and describe what the data set shows.

3. Use the graph to determine the maximum allowed time for a sound level of 97dB.

Part B: What Can Be Done?

4. With your group, discuss ideas you have for reducing your chance of developing NIHL. Make a list of strategies in your science notebook.

5. With your group, go through the list of strategies from the previous step and identify types of activities for which each strategy might succeed.

6. For each person described in the profiles below, use the "Federal Noise Standards" table to decide
   a. if they have a high-, medium-, or low-level risk for NIHL.
   b. why you gave them the rank.
   c. what could be done to protect their hearing.

José

José is an active middle school student who recently has had trouble hearing. When he went to the doctor, she didn't find any structural problems or inflammation in José's ears. She sent him for a hearing test, which showed he has some difficulty hearing higher frequencies in one ear. It is not clear at this time whether his hearing will return or the exact cause of the hearing loss. José will continue to undergo tests to determine the cause. In his free time, José reads, plays drums in a band, and often listens to music played loudly on his MP3 player with the earpiece in his right ear only.

Leon

Leon is 68 years old and just retired from his work as an engineer. He has always loved anything electronic, including games and robots. As a child he was fascinated by robots, a passion that led him to study robotic engineering in graduate school. His other love is music, and he goes to concerts regularly. He loves rock concerts as much as symphony concerts. He has been a band technician for many years, and when he noticed ringing in his ears that wasn't going away, he started getting concerned. Over the years, he has lost some hearing but has only recently noticed it. In particular, he has trouble understanding women when they are talking to him. His doctor has told him that he is a candidate to wear hearing aids.

Shannon

Shannon is a middle-aged woman who has worked at a paper mill for 10 years. Lately, her work has involved running the big trucks that pull the felled trees into the mill entrance. Her favorite part of the paper mill is watching the massive automated machines run paper rolls at high speed. She knows she should wear ear protection because she has some hearing loss at 3,000–6,000 Hz but admits she occasionally forgets to bring them to work.

Sophie

Sophie is a high school student with congenital deafness in both ears, which means she was born with little hearing. The cause of her deafness is most likely genetic as her father is also deaf. She has some hearing in one ear, and she would like to protect it. She has studied lipreading and had speech training, which is helpful in her everyday life but not particularly natural for her. She is most comfortable communicating through American Sign Language (ASL), which she learned from her parents and at school. She wonders if she might be making her hearing worse when she hangs out with her brother, who loves to take her to college soccer games.

ANALYSIS

1. List the people in the profiles from highest to lowest risk of further hearing loss, and explain how you chose their rank.

2. What would you recommend for the following people to help them protect their hearing?
   a. Snowmobile driver
   b. Concertgoer
   c. Hairstylist
   d. MP3 user

3. Ear protection is rated by how much noise reduction, in decibels, the device provides. The table on the next page shows the noise reduction of a pair of headphones at various frequencies. If you

were to choose ear protection for a firefighter who is exposed to a 1,500-Hz fire truck siren at 120 dB, would you choose this pair?

If yes, explain why the design will adequately protect the firefighter while driving with the siren turned on. If no, explain in what way the headphones are inadequate.

Headphone data

Frequency (Hz)	Noise Reduction (decibel)
125	22.1
250	27.9
500	34.9
1,000	35.8
2,000	37.3
3,150	41.4
4,000	42.3
6,000	41.6
8,000	41.2

4. Look at the photo above of the firefighter wearing the over-the-ear style of hearing protection. Compare it with the in-the-ear earplugs shown below. The over-the-ear style does a better job blocking out noise than the earplugs. Explain how the structure of the over-the-ear hearing protection contributes to its better function.

5. What kinds of things should be done to make people aware of the common risks to their hearing?

6. **Reflection:** How does your own risk compare with the case studies in this activity? Explain how you will or will not change your behavior based on what you have learned here.

5 Telephone Model

THERE ARE TWO major methods of transmitting information with waves. The first is an **analog** signal, which is a stream of a continuously changing value, such as air pressure, that is sent and received in its original form. An example of an analog signal is sound traveling across the room from one person to another. Analog has been used for decades, in part, because it does not require a microprocessor to transmit information. More recently, analog signals have been generated or converted to digital signals using a microprocessor. A **digital** signal uses a code system to represent information. For example, information in a song is converted to a series of 0s and 1s before the song is transmitted. After the code is received, a device recreates the song by converting the code back into the analog format. In this activity, you will model how analog and digital signals are transmitted over a distance.

GUIDING QUESTION

Which type of signal, analog or digital, is more reliable?

MATERIALS

For each group of four students

- 2 paper cups
- 1 cord, 4-m
- 1 cord, 2-m
- 1 toothpick, broken in half
- 1 pencil

27th President of the United States William Howard Taft using an analog "candlestick" telephone.

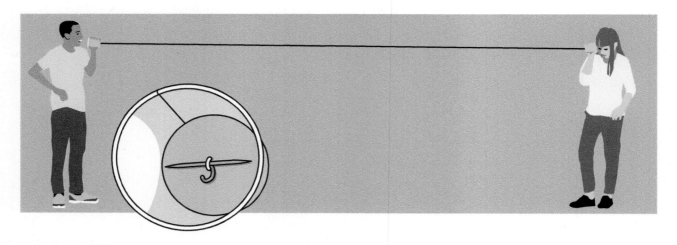

PROCEDURE

1. Build a "telephone" by connecting a set of two paper cups on a 4-m cord, as shown above.

2. With the cord stretched tight, alternate with your partner talking into the telephone at a consistent noise level while the other one listens. Listen for your partner's voice with your eyes closed and your finger in your exposed ear.

3. With the cord stretched tight, alternate with your partner tapping a pattern onto the bottom of the cup with the back of a pencil. When your partner hears the pattern, they should repeat it back to you. Reverse roles and try it again.

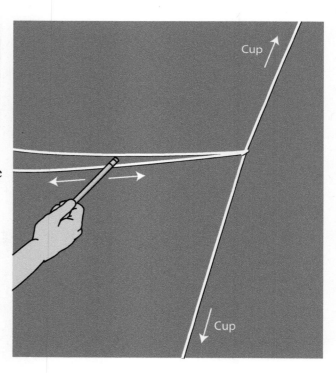

4. Attach the additional 2-m cord, as shown on the right, to model noise in the communication.

5. Repeat Steps 2 and 3 but have a third student create noise by running a pencil up and down the noise cord as shown in the diagram to the right.

6. Share your results with the class. Rank the four ways you transmitted information through the cups, as listed below, from the most (1) to the least (4) accurate transmission of sound.

Speaking without noise

Tapping without noise

Speaking with noise

Tapping with noise

ANALYSIS

1. Compare the transmission of voice and tapping in the activity. Which was understandable when there was
   a. no noise?

   b. noise?

2. In the diagrams below, which models analog (voice) and which models digital (taps) signals transmitted through the telephone in the investigation? Explain what experiences you had in the activity that informed your choice.

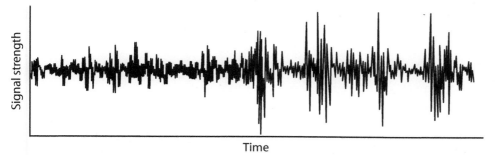

Diagram A

Diagram B

3. Look at the diagrams below that model noise in the waves from item 2. Is it easier to interpret the original wave in the analog or digital model? Use the diagrams to explain why noise can be more of a problem for one kind of signal over the other.

4. How could technology have been used to improve the results of the experiment in this activity?

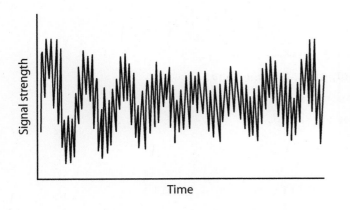

Diagram C

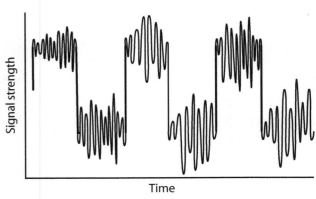

Diagram D

EXTENSION

Research the history of telephones. Investigate how they have evolved from wired to wireless and from analog to digital. Create a summary from information found in written text and media/visual displays.

6 Analog And Digital Technology

READING

SOUND WAVES, LIKE those produced when you speak, transmit energy from one place to another. However, sound can only be heard for a certain distance. You have experienced this whenever you have heard a sound fade as you move away from the source of the sound. Devices, such as radios and telephones, were invented so that music, conversations, and speeches made at one location could be heard at distant locations. And records were invented so that sounds could be stored and played back on a record player at any time and in any location.

Sound is a continuous, or analog, signal. Records, the first radios, and the first telephones used analog technology. But since the 1970s, the digital transmission and storage of information has grown. Modern cell phones, CDs and MP3 players, and hearing aids all depend on digital technology.

GUIDING QUESTION

What is the difference between digital and analog transmission?

PROCEDURE

1. Use the Listen, Stop, and Write strategy to help you with this reading. Listen as your teacher reads aloud. When they stop reading, close your book. Write down the main ideas you just heard.

Listen as your teacher reads aloud.

Stop when you see this yellow pencil and close your book.

Write down the main ideas you just heard.

Communication Waves

Information can be sent with either an analog or digital signal. Both kinds of signal depend on the transmission of waves. To record sound with an analog recorder, a microphone transmits the compressions and rarefactions of the sound wave to a device that records the

exact pattern onto a metallic tape. In analog transmission, the signal is a stream of information that varies continuously when it is converted to a mechanical or electrical format.

Binary Conversion

0	0011 0000	O	0100 1111	m	0110 1101
1	0011 0001	P	0101 0000	n	0110 1110
2	0011 0010	Q	0101 0001	o	0110 1111
3	0011 0011	R	0101 0010	p	0111 0000
4	0011 0100	S	0101 0011	q	0111 0001
5	0011 0101	T	0101 0100	r	0111 0010
6	0011 0110	U	0101 0101	s	0111 0011
7	0011 0111	V	0101 0110	t	0111 0100
8	0011 1000	W	0101 0111	u	0111 0101
9	0011 1001	X	0101 1000	v	0111 0110
A	0100 0001	Y	0101 1001	w	0111 0111
B	0100 0010	Z	0101 1010	x	0111 1000
C	0100 0011	a	0110 0001	y	0111 1001
D	0100 0100	b	0110 0010	z	0111 1010
E	0100 0101	c	0110 0011	.	0010 1110
F	0100 0110	d	0110 0100	,	0010 0111
G	0100 0111	e	0110 0101	:	0011 1010
H	0100 1000	f	0110 0110	;	0011 1011
I	0100 1001	g	0110 0111	?	0011 1111
J	0100 1010	h	0110 1000	!	0010 0001
K	0100 1011	I	0110 1001	'	0010 1100
L	0100 1100	j	0110 1010	"	0010 0010
M	0100 1101	k	0110 1011	(	0010 1000
N	0100 1110	l	0110 1100	)	0010 1001
				space	0010 0000

The cassette tape (above) holds an analog sound recording on its metallic tape. The chart (below) shows the conversion of letters and numbers into digital binary code.

A digital signal is produced when an analog wave is translated into a series of numbers before it is transmitted. Most often, the information is represented by a series of two values, 0 or 1. When the signal arrives at its destination, the signal is reconstructed as shown in the diagram below. This technology has improved to the point where the advantages of digital transmission are significant. Digital communications dominate radio, fiber optics, and computer networks.

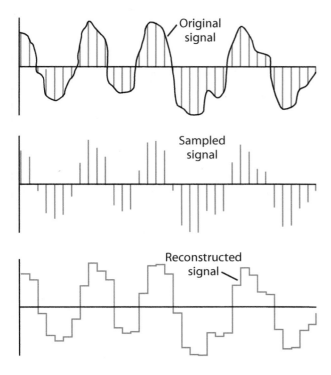

Diagram of analog to digital conversion.

Sample Rate

When you make a call on a cell phone, the analog sound waves produced when you speak are converted to digital signals for transmission. The transmitted sound wave is represented by a code of zeros and ones. This is done by measuring, or sampling, the amplitude of the wave at various places, as shown in the diagram on the following page. The **sampling rate** is the number of measurements taken per second to represent the wave. The accuracy of a digital signal is only as good as its sampling rate. At low sampling rates, a digital signal will not accurately represent the analog signal. When sampling rates are increased, however, the accuracy of a digital signal improves. As digital technology has improved, sampling rates for digital signals have steadily increased. Sampling rates vary depending on the use. For example, the sampling rate for recording sound using a wireless microphone or telephone is typically 8,000 Hz. The sampling rate for recording a digital video can be upwards of 192,000 Hz. The diagram below shows how the accuracy of the recreated wave is better with a higher sampling rate.

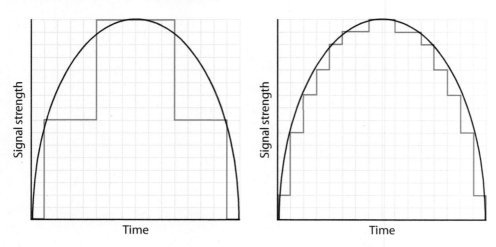

Diagram of a relatively lower sampling rate (left) and a higher sampling rate (right).

Attenuation

Both analog and digital waves lose signal strength during transmission. The gradual loss of intensity of a wave as it travels is called **attenuation**. When the wave arrives at its destination, the signal needs to be boosted to return it to its original strength, as shown on the diagrams on the next page. An amplifier does this by using energy from a power supply to increase the amplitude of the wave. The amplifier increases the amplitude of a wave without changing its frequency.

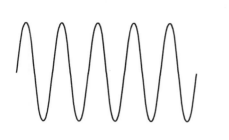

Original signal

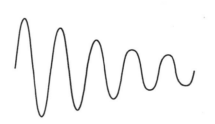

Attenuated signal

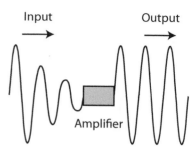

Boosted signal

Advantages of Digital

Digital signals can now be sampled frequently enough for extremely accurate transmission. However, for music, some argue that it does not capture the full richness and complexity of analog transmission. Despite this objection, there are significant advantages to digital signals. The main advantage of digital signals over analog signals for long distance transmission is that noise interference has less impact on digital transmission. The quality of any signal decreases the farther it travels due to the increasing interference of unwanted noise on the signal. However, digital signals are less susceptible to distortion over long distances because they use a discrete on–off code that is clearer to read. It is easier to interpret an on–off signal that has some noise in it than an analog signal, as shown in the diagrams below.

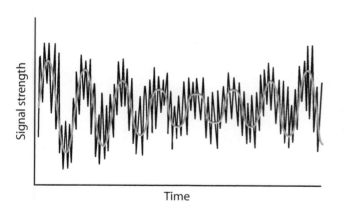

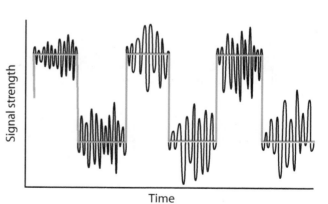

Digital vs analog noise diagrams

Another advantage of digital over analog relates to the formats used for the recordings. Digital recordings, such as those stored on a computer, tend to last much longer than analog recordings, such as vinyl music records. Analog recordings use physical parts to transmit data, and physical parts can wear out. For instance, a record player depends on a needle to convert the information on the recording back into sound. Over time, the friction between the needle and vinyl record wears down the grooves in the record, which lowers the quality of the sound. Digital recordings use electronic parts, like lasers, that do not degrade over time. Another key advantage is that digital recordings can be reproduced at the same quality as the original.

As a result of these advantages, digital technology has become the preferred method for transmitting and storing information. Digital technology has exploded since the early 1990s. Now, nearly all transmissions are digital.

Noise and Clarity

Speech, like music, has many frequencies and volumes combined into one signal. You may listen to music using headphones when there is external noise interfering with what you want to hear. Interference tends to affect the higher frequency sounds in music and speech. When this happens, it is tempting to turn up the volume to better hear the high-frequency sounds. This can be dangerous, however, because the lower frequency sounds are also being turned up. The result is some small improvement in hearing the high-frequency sounds at the risk of too much overall energy entering the ear, which can damage it. This is an issue with lower quality headphones, because people tend to turn up the volume to unsafe levels to hear over external noise.

Headphones are often turned up significantly when users are in noisy places.

Hearing Aid Technology

One common device that transmits sound waves is the hearing aid. The first electronic hearing aids, developed in the 1950s, used analog technology. In the 1960s, hearing aids small enough to be worn behind the ear became available. Over the next 20 years, various advances reduced the size and improved performance of hearing aids. The early hearing aid had a microphone, amplifier, electronic filters that changed the signal to match the wearer's deficits, and a speaker. Although the hearing aid could be adjusted to amplify certain frequencies based on a person's hearing loss, the device would amplify voice and background noise equally. Because of this, the first generation of analog hearing aids had limited use in noisy places, such as restaurants or on the street.

In the mid-1990s, digital hearing aids were introduced. Nearly all hearing aids used today are digital. A digital hearing aid converts sound into a digital format. The microprocessor in the hearing aid adjusts the signal to make up for the wearer's deficits and then converts it back to sound. A sophisticated hearing aid can detect and amplify the softest speech sound while simultaneously canceling out unwanted background noise. In addition to adjusting for the wearer's specific kind of hearing loss, the microprocessor in the hearing aid adapts to different environments, from a quiet room to a crowded restaurant or a windy beach.

People who have severe hearing loss not helped by a hearing aid may consider a cochlear implant. The cochlear implant is named after the cochlea, the snail-shaped organ filled with fluid in the inner ear. This part of the ear has sensory cells that detect sound and send signals to the auditory nerve. A cochlear implant is a digital device

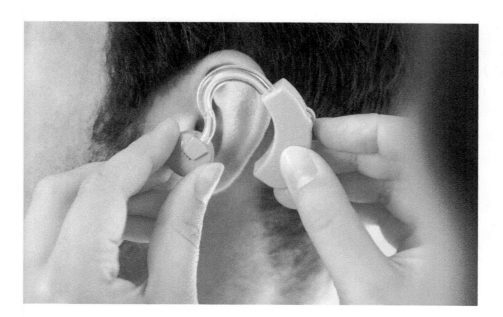

surgically placed in the ear that replaces these damaged sensory cells. The implant bypasses the damaged cells and directly stimulates the auditory nerve. A cochlear implant does not restore normal hearing. Instead, it can give a person with hearing loss a useful representation of sounds in the environment and aid in speech recognition.

Digital hearing aids were invented in the 1990s through a collaboration between the National Institute of Health (NIH), the Department of Veterans Affairs (VA), and the National Aeronautics and Space Administration (NASA). This work resulted in ongoing partnerships between neuroscientists, audiologists, engineers, and industry leaders. The advances in hearing aid technology have continued to influence the work of scientists, and vice versa. One area of ongoing research for this group is exploring ways to provide an option for those with severe hearing loss to successfully use a hearing aid. This group of people may benefit from new technologies because even the most sophisticated hearing aids, including cochlear implants, are not effective for them.

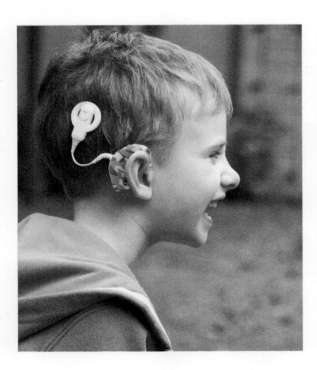

Boy with cochlear implant

ANALYSIS

1. Explain the difference between analog and digital sound transmission.

2. Use what you learned from your hands-on investigation in Activity 5, "Telephone Model," and from the text and diagrams in this activity to explain

   a. why noise is more of a problem for long-distance analog signals than for digital ones.

   b. why digital signals are a more reliable way to encode and transmit information than analog signals.

3. What are the advantages of digital hearing aids over analog ones? Explain how the structures of the hearing aids contribute to how they function.

4. Examine the two methods below for storing and reproducing music. Explain why the CD is a more reliable way to encode and transmit the information than the record player.

   a. A record player has a sensitive needle that vibrates directly in a groove on a spinning vinyl disc. The vibration that travels through the needle is amplified to produce the sound.

   b. A CD has a continuous track of microscopic bumps in a plastic disc that is read by a laser, which uses a small computer to reconstruct the sound from the coded bumps.

Record player and CDs

5. Choose a digital device other than those discussed in this activity. Research the history of the device and describe how the device has advanced science and scientific investigation.

EXTENSION

Find a multimedia presentation about Deaf culture and the use of sign language in that community. Investigate the perspective of the Deaf community on the use of hearing aids and cochlear implants.

7 Another Kind Of Wave

INVESTIGATION

SOUND IS ONE of many kinds of waves. Other common waves include those on the surface of water, light waves, radio waves, and seismic waves. Digital sound transmission, as described in the last activity, involves more than one kind of wave. For example, a sound wave could be transformed into a microwave for transmission. When it arrives at its destination, the digital information encoded on the microwave is reconstructed back into the sound wave.

All waves share some of the same characteristics, but they also differ in certain ways. A good example of this becomes apparent when comparing sound and light. As with all waves, sound and light both carry energy. Like sound, light is an integral part of our everyday life. However, there are important differences. One difference is that light travels over 800,000 times faster in air than does sound. Another difference is that light is not a longitudinal wave like sound but, instead, behaves as a transverse wave. A **transverse** wave consists of vibrations that are perpendicular to the direction that the energy travels. A transverse wave may travel through a medium, such as secondary waves (s-waves) in an earthquake, or without a medium, such as light through a vacuum. This means that a transverse wave does not have compressions and rarefactions like sound. In this activity, you will model the characteristics of transverse waves using a long metal spring.

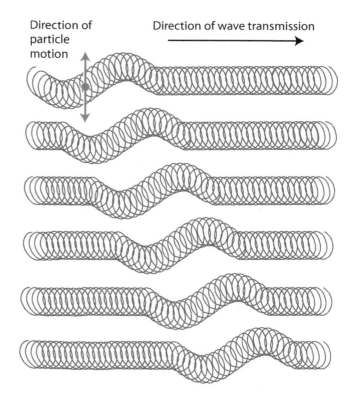

Direction of particle motion

Direction of wave transmission

Transverse wave

GUIDING QUESTION

What are the characteristics of a transverse wave?

MATERIALS

For each group of four students

    1 long metal spring

For each student

    1 pair of safety goggles

    1 sheet of graph paper

SAFETY

Handle the springs with care and never let go suddenly when the spring is under tension. If released when tension is being applied, the spring can move rapidly and unpredictably and could scratch someone. Wear safety goggles to protect your eyes from such an event.

PROCEDURE

Part A: Wave Pulses

1. Put the spring on the floor or a long table, holding the ends about 2 m apart.

2. Near one end of the spring, pull a coil away from its resting position toward one side of the spring, as shown below. When everyone is ready, release the coil to make a wave pulse.

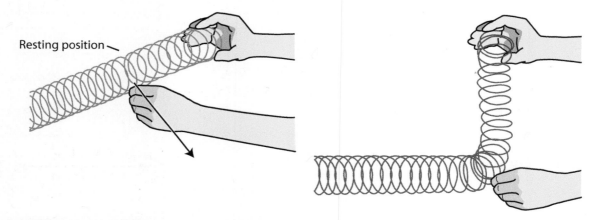

3. All group members should observe the pulse as it travels down the spring.

4. Record the group's observations in your science notebook.

5. Create additional pulses by pulling and releasing more coils. Each time, observe and record what happens as the pulse travels down the spring.

6. Predict what would happen if you pulled the coil farther from the resting position, or increased the amplitude, before releasing it.

7. Test your prediction and record the results in your science notebook. Draw and label two diagrams that show a comparison of the waves.

8. Describe any evidence you saw that the transferred energy increased when you increased the amplitude.

9. Change roles and repeat Steps 2–7 with the spring ends held about 4 m apart. Record any differences that you observe.

Part B: Transverse Waves

10. Generate a transverse wave instead of a single pulse by continuously moving one end of the spring to the left and right. Record your observations in your science notebook.

11. Vary the amplitude of the wave from small to large. All group members should observe and record what happens as the wave travels down the spring.

12. Vary the frequency of the wave from low to high. All group members should observe and record what happens as the wave travels down the spring.

13. Draw and label four diagrams that show a comparison of the waves from the previous two steps.

14. On one of your wave diagrams, label the wavelength. The **wavelength** of the wave is the length of one wave cycle, as shown in the diagrams below.

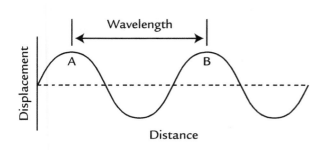
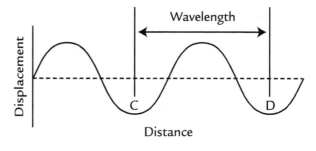

15. Repeat making a wave with a low frequency and compare it with one with a high frequency. Compare the wavelengths of the two waves as they travel down the spring.

16. Using what you observed in the previous step, draw two wave diagrams. In the first diagram, draw a wave with a low frequency. In the second diagram, draw a wave with a higher frequency. Label the frequencies and wavelengths in both diagrams.

17. In your group, discuss what you observed about the relationship between the frequency and wavelength. Decide which of the following graphs best describes what you observed and modeled in your diagrams.

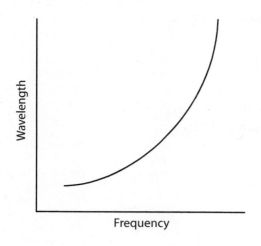 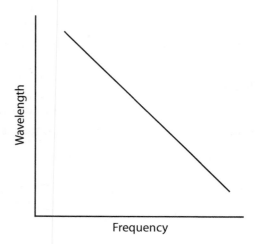

ANALYSIS

1. Describe what happened when
   a. the wave pulses reached the end of the spring.
   b. the transverse wave reached the end of the spring.

2. What happened when the spring was stretched to double its length?

3. What happened to the amplitude of the wave pulse when it traveled along the spring? Suggest an explanation for your observations.

4 Do you think that sound also has a wavelength? Explain why or why not.

5. Look at the diagram shown on the right of a wave made with a spring.

    a. Describe the motion of the spring at points B and C.

    b. Is the energy transfer of the wave parallel or perpendicular to the motion of the spring at point B? Explain.

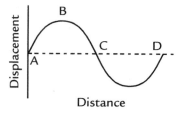

6. Trace the diagram from the previous question above, and then

    a. draw what the wave would look like if the amplitude was doubled.

    b. draw what the wave would look like if the frequency was doubled.

    c. draw what the wave would look like if the wavelength was doubled.

7. Make two tables like the ones below, and fill in the missing diagrams to show changes in wavelength and frequency. Then explain what your diagrams model.

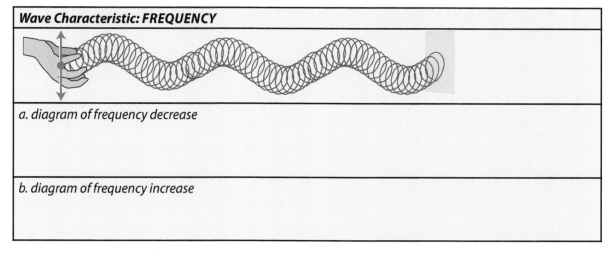

Wave Characteristic: WAVELENGTH

a. diagram of a wavelength increase

b. diagram of a wavelength decrease

Wave Characteristic: FREQUENCY

a. diagram of frequency decrease

b. diagram of frequency increase

8. For a wave of a given speed, what is the relationship between the wavelength and the frequency? Use your diagrams from the activity and the model from the previous item to look for patterns.

9. A transverse wave with constant speed has an increase in amplitude over time, as shown in the left-hand column of the table below. Some of the data for energy and wavelength is missing.

Transverse wave data		
Amplitude (m)	Energy (J)	Wavelength (m)
1	10	0.3
2	40	0.3
3	90	0.3
4		
5		

a. Look at the patterns in the data and predict the missing energies and wavelengths of the wave. In your science notebook, copy the last two rows of the table and complete the data. Then explain the pattern you followed to fill in the data.

b. Make a graph of amplitude (x-axis) vs. energy (y-axis) that includes all five times. Make sure to label your graph.

c. Use your graph to predict the energy and wavelength for the amplitude of 7 m.

EXTENSION

Investigate a *standing wave* and model them with your long spring.

8 *Wave Reflection*

LABORATORY

I N PREVIOUS ACTIVITIES, you explored how waves have certain properties, such as frequency or speed. In this activity, you will explore the wave property of **reflection** the bouncing of a wave off an object. Reflection is a property that applies to all kinds of waves, including both sound and light.

A mirror reflects light off its surface.

GUIDING QUESTION

What kind of surface makes a good reflector?

MATERIALS

Part A

For each group of four students

> 2 cardboard tubes

Part B

For each group of four students

> 1 light station
>
> 1 single-slit mask
>
> 1 triple-slit mask
>
> 1 plane mirror
>
> 2 plane mirror holders
>
> 1 curved mirror
>
> 1 curved mirror holder
>
> 1 angle card
>
> 1 index card

Acoustical tiles are used in large spaces to reduce the reflection of sound off the ceiling.

PROCEDURE

Part A: Reflecting Sound

1. In your group of four, find a hard, smooth surface, such as a wall or white board.

2. Position the end of one of the cardboard tubes about 20 cm from the smooth surface, and angle it at about 45 degrees to the surface, as shown in the diagram below.

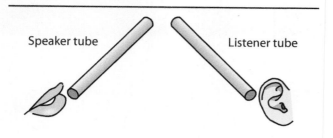

Speaker tube   Listener tube

3. Have one member of your group speak softly into the end of the tube that is farthest from the smooth surface.

4. Have another member of your group listen through the end of the second tube, which is held 20 cm away and pointed towards the smooth surface, as shown in the diagram in Step 2.

5. Keep the speaker tube in the same position while trying to find the position of the listener tube that allows the speaker's voice to be heard the clearest.

6. When you have found the best position for the speaker tube, have another member of your group draw a diagram to record the positions of the two tubes and the smooth surface.

7. Move the listener tube to a different angle from the wall and repeat Steps 3–6. In your science notebook, record any patterns you observe about the positions of the two tubes.

8. Repeat Steps 3–7 using a soft surface instead of a hard surface. Record your observations in your science notebook.

Part B: Reflecting Light

9. Set up the light station using the diagram below.

10. Stand a plane mirror so that it is upright on the mirror line of the angle card.

11. Based on your experiences in Part A, predict where you think the light will go when it is turned on if it travels to the mirror along line 1L.

12. Test your prediction and record your results in your science notebook.

13. Design an investigation to determine the relationship between the incoming light ray and the reflected ray.

14. Get your teacher's approval and conduct your experiment. Record your results in a table.

15. Discuss your findings with your class.

16. Adjust the light station by replacing the single slit with the triple slit.

17. In your group, predict what would happen if you aim the three rays of light from the triple slit at an angle towards the mirror. In your science notebook, draw a diagram to represent your group's prediction. Make sure to include the reasoning behind your prediction.

18. Test your prediction and record your observations by drawing a diagram in your science notebook.

19. Replace the plane mirror with the curved mirror and repeat Steps 17–18.

20. Replace the curved mirror with the white index card and repeat Steps 17–18.

ANALYSIS

1. What patterns did you notice about the angle of the listener tube compared with the angle of the speaker tube?

2. Describe the relationship between the angle that a ray hits a mirror and the angle that the same ray reflects off
   a. a plane mirror.
   b. a curved mirror.

3. Was light reflected off the white index card? Explain how you know.

4. Which surface, a shiny or bumpy one, do you think would be best used for the ceiling of a concert hall? Explain your choice.

5. The diagram below represents a highly magnified image of the surface of the index card. The five lines with arrows represent rays of light hitting the card. Copy the diagram and then
   a. draw the rays of light that are reflected from the card.
   b. explain why the surface of the card does not appear shiny like a mirror.

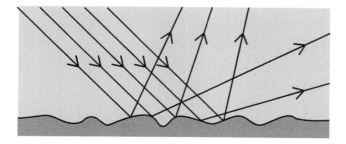

6. Explain why the ears of some mammals are bowl-shaped.

7. If only some of the light that hits an object is reflected, predict what might happen to the rest of the light.

9 *Refraction Of Light*

LABORATORY

IN GENERAL, LIGHT travels in a straight line. This occurs when light is **transmitted**, which is when light passes through a vacuum or a material. However, at the boundary between two transparent materials, the light can be redirected. This phenomenon is called **refraction**. Refraction occurs when a wave passes from one material to another, such as from air to glass. Upon entering the second material, the light travels at a higher or lower speed depending on the properties of the second material such as temperature, pressure, and density. As the speed changes, the direction of travel through the material also changes if it hits the boundary at an angle other than perpendicular. This can be observed when a pencil inserted in a glass of water appears to bend at the boundary where the water meets the air.

GUIDING QUESTION

How does light behave at the boundary between two different materials?

MATERIALS

For each group of four students

- 1 light station
- 1 single-slit mask
- 1 beam blocker with stand
- 1 semicircular container
- 1 protractor
- 1 ruler
- 1 sheet of white paper
- milky water

For each student

- 1 Student Sheet 9.1, "Refraction Measurements"
- 1 Student Sheet 9.2, "Total Internal Reflection Measurements"
- 1 sheet graph paper

PROCEDURE

Part A: Refraction

1. Place the container with milky water on Student Sheet 9.1, "Refraction Measurements."

2. With your partner, predict what will happen to the path of a beam of light when it is pointed directly down the center line toward the dot and through the container full of milky water, as shown in the diagram below.

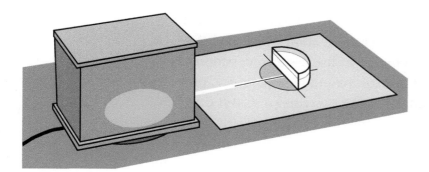

3. Test your prediction and record your results on Student Sheet 9.1.

4. Design an investigation to learn what happens to the direction of the beam of light when it hits the boundary of the glass or container at an angle between 0 and 90 degrees. In your investigation, make sure to measure the

   • **angle of incidence**, or the angle between the incoming light ray and the normal line.

   • **angle of refraction**, or the angle between the normal line and the path the light travels in the new medium.

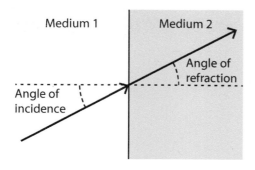

5. After getting approval from your teacher, conduct the investigation and record your results.

6. Graph the angle of incidence (x-axis) vs. the angle of refraction (y-axis).

7. With your group, make a statement that explains the pattern in your results, and record the statement in your science notebook.

Part B: Total Internal Reflection

8. With your partner, design an investigation to find the critical angle of the milky water. The **critical angle** is equal to the angle of incidence that produces a 90-degree angle of refraction. When the incident ray is greater than the critical angle, the light traveling from an optically denser to less dense medium no longer transmits through the material. Instead, it is completely reflected back into the denser material. When the light no longer travels through to the next medium in this way, it is called **total internal reflection**. In this activity, the optically denser medium is the milky water and the less dense medium is the air.

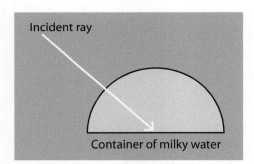

9. Use Student Sheet 9.2, "Total Internal Reflection Measurements," to collect your data.

10. Share your results with the class.

ANALYSIS

1. Draw a diagram with labels that shows how the light traveled through the milky water when it was

   a. directed down the normal line.

   b. directed at an angle.

2. Look at the data below that show the refraction of light from one medium to another for various materials.

Refraction of common materials

Material	Critical angle (degrees)	Optical Density (index of refraction)	Incident angle (degrees)	Refraction angle (degrees)
Water	50	1.3	20	15.2
Sugar solution (40%)	46	1.4	20	14.1
Acrylic	42	1.5	20	13.2
Flint glass	39	1.6	20	12.3

Your friend looks at these data and says, "I see a general trend showing that as the optical density of a material increases, the critical angle also increases." Do you agree or disagree with your friend? Explain your opinion using evidence from the table.

3. The principle of total internal reflection is used in fiber optic technology. A wave signal is sent down a glass tube at greater than the critical angle so that it is reflected off the interior of the tube as it travels. Copy the close-up diagram of a fiber optic cable below. Draw arrow(s) that show a possible ray that is totally internally reflected through the tube.

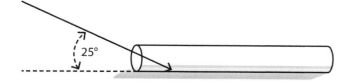

25°

4. The functioning of the human eyeball depends on the refraction of light. When light comes into the eye, first the cornea and then the lens refracts the light so that it focuses on the retina. The lens is flexible and is controlled by muscles in the eye. The curvature of the lens changes in order to focus objects at different distances. If the lens does not refract properly, the light rays do not come together at a point on the retina.

When the light focuses past the retina, the person will have blurry vision at close distances. This person would be considered farsighted. Farsightedness can be corrected with eyeglasses or contact lenses that refract the light inwards before it enters the eye. The opposite problem, or nearsightedness, occurs when the light entering the eye comes to a point before it hits the retina. It results in blurry vision at farther distances. This is corrected by refracting the light outwards before it enters the eye.

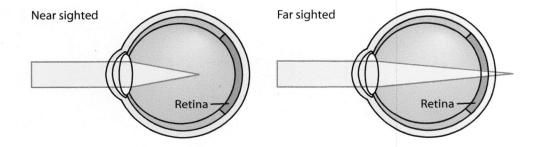

Near sighted

Far sighted

Retina

Retina

Which one of the following eyeglass lenses can be used to make the light fall on the retina of a nearsighted person, as shown below.? Draw a diagram that shows the lens, the eye, and two rays of light converging on the retina.

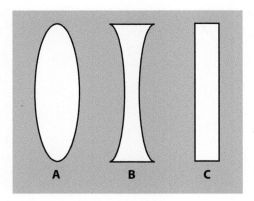

A   B   C

10 Comparing Colors

LABORATORY

DURING FIRST PERIOD, *Jenna noticed that her friend José looked worried. After class she asked, "José, is everything okay with you?"*

José replied, "Well, actually, I'm a little distracted because my favorite great-aunt, Tía Ana, is having eye surgery."

"Surgery!" replied Jenna. "What happened?"

José explained, "Everything began to look a bit blurry and she became sensitive to the glare of lights, especially at night. When she went to her doctor, she learned that the lens in one of her eyes had developed a cataract. Today the eye surgeon is going to take out the cloudy lens in her right eye and put in an artificial one. I know it is a common procedure, but I am worried anyway."

Sighted people use their eyes for almost everything they do, and so it is important to take care of them. One thing that hurts our eyes is too much exposure to the sun. Even people with limited vision may damage their eyes further by exposing them to too much sunlight.

In this activity, you will explore some of the characteristics of white light to investigate what might have damaged Tía Ana's eyesight. White light can be separated into the **visible light spectrum**, which is the scientific name for the colors of the rainbow.

GUIDING QUESTION

How are the colors of the visible light spectrum similar to and different from each other?

MATERIALS

For each pair of students

1 Phospho-box
1 card with a star-shaped cutout
1 colored-film card
1 timer

PROCEDURE

Part A: The Visible Light Spectrum

1. Observe how your teacher splits white light into the colors of the visible spectrum.

2. List the colors that you see in the order that they appear.

3. Describe whether the colors blend from one to the next or have distinct boundaries between them.

4. Which color of light seems to be
   a. the brightest?
   b. the least bright?

Part B: Colored Light

5. Open the lid of the Phospho-box and examine the bottom of the box. The strip on the bottom of the Phospho-box is sensitive to a particular short-wavelength wave. Sketch and describe what you observe.

6. Close the Phospho-box and turn it over so that the top with the viewing slit is on the table. Slip the card with the star-shaped cutout into the card-insert location at the bottom of the box, as shown below. Leave the box in this position for 30 s.

7. Turn the Phospho-box right side up, open the top, and let light hit the entire bottom of the box for 20 s.

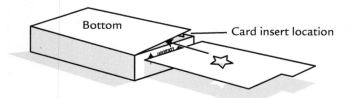

8. Close the top of the Phospho-box and remove the card with the star-shaped cutout. Quickly look through the viewing slit and record your observations.

9. Turn over the Phospho-box as you did in Step 6. Lay the colored-film card on top of the Phospho-box.

10. Describe or sketch what you see. Rank the colors from brightest to least bright.

11. Describe or sketch what you predict you will observe if you repeat Steps 6–8 using the colored-film card instead of the card with the star-shaped cutout.

12. Repeat Steps 6–8, but use the colored-film card instead of the card with the star-shaped cutout.

13. Rank each color of the cutout shape according to how brightly it caused the strip on the bottom of the Phospho-box to glow.

14. Describe or sketch what you predict you will observe if you repeat Steps 6–8 with the colored-film card, but this time let the sunlight hit the bottom of the box for 40 s.

15. Repeat Steps 6–8 with the colored-film card, but this time let the light hit the bottom of the Phospho-box for 40 s. Record your results in your science notebook.

A rainbow shows the colors of the visible light spectrum.

ANALYSIS

1. What is the purpose of the card with the star-shaped cutout?

2. How do you think the colored-film card changes the white light into colored light? Describe how you might test your ideas to see if they are correct.

3. Why do you think only some colors make the strip on the bottom of the Phospho-box glow? Explain.

4. Is there enough evidence information that supports or refutes a claim that supports the idea that the higher-energy colors of white light are damaging Tía Ana's eyes? Explain your answer.

5. Which characteristic of a light wave explored in this activity affects the amount of energy that it carries?

6. Sunglass lenses are an example of a material that blocks some white light and some other short-wavelength light that is harmful to the eyes. Examine the transmission graphs about three pairs of sunglasses below.

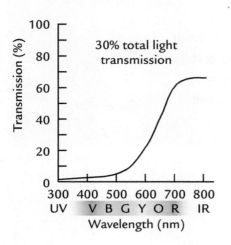 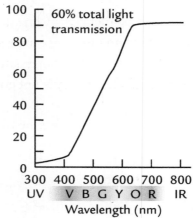 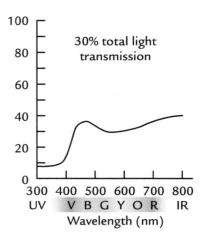

a. Which lens has the best protection for the eyes against high-energy waves? Explain how you decided.

b. The price for each pair of sunglasses is shown below. Which pair would you buy? Why? Describe any trade-offs you made in your choice. A trade-off is an outcome given up to gain another outcome.

Lens 1: $80

Lens 2: $10

Lens 3: $20

11 *Selective Transmission*

LABORATORY

I N PREVIOUS ACTIVITIES, you saw how waves, such as sound and light, transmit energy from one place to another. Light can be transmitted through one material into another. Any light that is not transmitted through a boundary between two materials is either reflected or absorbed by the object it hits. Like sound waves, light waves are reflected when light bounces off an object, either sent in one direction or scattered in many directions. When we see an object, we are seeing the light it reflects. Light waves are **absorbed** when light enters an object and does not exit the object again as light. The energy is not gone but is now in the object. This absorbed light is usually converted into heat that warms up the object. In this activity, you will investigate the transmission, reflection, and absorption of waves from the sun that are not visible to the human eye.

Sunlight is selectively transmitted through the stained glass window.

GUIDING QUESTION

What part of sunlight is transmitted through selected films?

MATERIALS

For each group of four students

- 3 thermometers
- 3 UV detector cards
- 3 Phospho-boxes
- 1 Film A
- 1 Film B
- 1 Film C
- 1 timer
- masking tape

SAFETY NOTE

Do not look directly into the sun as it can permanently damage your eyes.

PROCEDURE

Part A: Comparing Temperatures

1. In your science notebook, create a data table similar to the one below.

Temperature Data			
Film	Initial temperature (°C)	Final temperature (°C)	Change in temperature (°C)
A			
B			
C			

2. Place one thermometer face up in the bottom of each of the boxes, and tape it in place so that it will not move. Place a film on each open box and secure it with tape, as shown in the diagram at right. Make sure to tape the film on all four sides to keep air from entering the box during testing.

3. Close the Phospho-box lids until you are ready to perform the experiment in the sun.

4. When in the sunlight, have one member of your group hold the closed Phospho-boxes together so they are oriented toward the sun in the same way. Do this so no shadow falls on the thermometer.

5. Record in the data table the initial temperature inside each box.

6. Have another group member open each box and expose it to the sun.

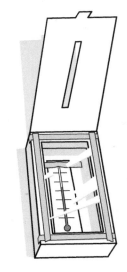

7. Hold or prop the boxes in this position for 5 min.

8. Record in the data table the final temperature inside each box.

9. Calculate the change in temperature for each thermometer. Record these data in your data table.

10. Rank each film from 1 (smallest change) to 3 (highest change). Record your results in your science notebook.

Part B: Comparing Ultraviolet

11. Gently remove the films and replace the thermometers with the UV detector cards. Replace the films as instructed in Step 2.

12. Make a new data table with titles changed accordingly.

13. Repeat Steps 3–10.

14. With your group, discuss if the results from Part A, Part B, or both give evidence for invisible waves transmitted into the Phospho-box.

ANALYSIS

1. Which film transmits the most energy? What is your evidence?

2. What evidence from this investigation supports the idea that sunlight contains invisible waves that behave similarly, but not identically, to visible light waves?

3. Films, like the ones used in this activity, are commonly put on glass windows as energy-saving devices and to prevent sun damage. If the costs of Films A, B, and C from this activity are those listed below, which material would you choose to put on
   a. your car windows?
   b. windows in a home located in a desert?
   c. windows in a home located in a snowy mountainous region?

   Explain your choices, citing the structure and function of the films. Explain any trade-offs you made.

   Film A: $20/m^2$

   Film B: $100/m^2$

   Film C: $50/m^2$

12 The Electromagnetic Spectrum

READING

SUNLIGHT IS A combination of light of various wavelengths. Some of the wavelengths can be seen and some cannot be seen by the human eye. The Reading in this activity explores the nature of these waves, which are electromagnetic. An **electromagnetic wave** transmits energy across distance as changing electrical and magnetic fields.

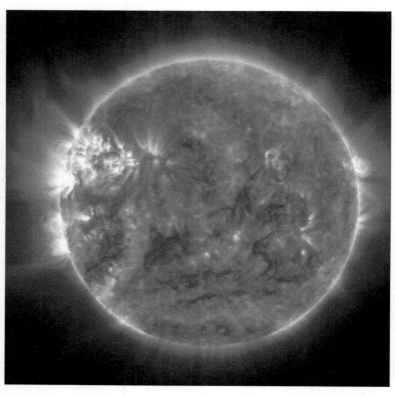

This image shows one wavelength of ultraviolet given off by the sun. This wavelength is not visible to the human eye but is typically colorized in blue.

GUIDING QUESTION

What are the characteristics of electromagnetic waves?

MATERIALS

For each student

    1 Student Sheet 12.1, "Anticipation Guide: The Electromagnetic Spectrum"

PROCEDURE

1. Fill in the Before column of Student Sheet 12.1, "Anticipation Guide: The Electromagnetic Spectrum."

2. Complete the Reading.

3. Fill in the After column of Student Sheet 12.1.

READING

Herschel's Famous Experiment

In 1800, German-born British musician and astronomer Sir Frederick William Herschel made a big discovery. While looking at the sun through colored lenses, he noted that some colors of light felt warmer than others. He wanted to learn more. He designed an experiment to try to measure the temperatures of the different colors of light.

In his experiment, Herschel used a prism, a triangular piece of glass to refract sunlight into the colors of the rainbow. When white light travels through a prism, each wavelength refracts a slightly different amount, creating a rainbow. Herschel first separated the light. Then he placed thermometers such that they were only struck by one color at a time. He noticed that red light caused a greater temperature rise than green or violet light, as shown in the diagram on the right. To his surprise, he also noticed that the temperature rose even more when the thermometer was in the unlit area just below the red end of the spectrum.

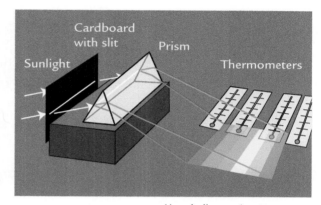

Herschel's experiment

Based on his results, Herschel reasoned that sunlight must contain invisible energy that can heat up objects. He called the energy "calorific rays" since calorific refers to heat. When he carried out other tests, Herschel found that calorific rays behaved just like visible light. They could be reflected, absorbed, or transmitted like waves. Scientists named this kind of light **infrared,** where the prefix *infra-* means below. This discovery made Herschel the first person to detect a type of electromagnetic wave not visible to humans.

Infrared heats up objects more than visible light because of its wavelength. When infrared hits an object, the molecules in the object often absorb infrared. The result is an increase in the molecules' energy, which makes the molecules move faster. Faster molecules lead to a warmer object. Not only do most objects readily absorb infrared, but warm objects also give it off.

Ultraviolet Energy

A year after the discovery of infrared, Johann Wilhelm Ritter in Germany decided to find out if there is energy beyond the violet end of the visible spectrum. He carried out an experiment like Herschel's. Instead of a thermometer, he aimed the light onto a special paper that turned black when exposed to light. The chemical on the paper, silver chloride, darkens more when hit by light from the violet end of the spectrum. When Ritter separated the light, the paper turned darkest just beyond the visible violet end of the spectrum. He first called his discovery "chemical rays" after the chemical reaction in the paper. Later this type of light just beyond the visible light spectrum became known as **ultraviolet** because the prefix *ultra-* means beyond.

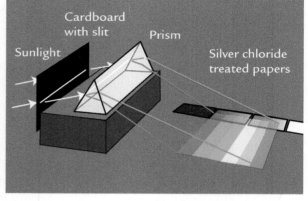

Ritter's experiment

Ritter's results stayed the same when he changed the amount of light shined on the paper. Reducing the brightness of the light is similar to reducing the intensity of a sound wave. Yet no matter how much Ritter dimmed the light, the paper turned black. This is because the reaction in the paper was due to the wavelength of the ultraviolet and not its brightness. Longer wavelength light of any brightness, such as visible light or infrared, does not turn the paper black. The paper only turns black when exposed to ultraviolet.

Despite its relatively high energy, ultraviolet can be helpful to humans. When human skin is exposed to ultraviolet energy, the body converts a chemical in the skin into vitamin D. Vitamin D is necessary for bone growth. Those people who lack sun exposure and whose diets lack vitamin D may develop a deficiency. This results in bone-growth problems in children or soft bones in adults. Low levels of vitamin D have been associated with cardiovascular disease, cognitive impairment, and cancer. One more benefit of ultraviolet is that it can be used to disinfect medical devices. The wavelength range of ultraviolet has enough energy to destroy bacteria, viruses, and molds.

At the same time, ultraviolet energy poses a danger to people and other living things. Its wavelength causes damage to living cells. Over time it can result in skin cancer and cataracts, like those in Tía Ana's eyes. Ultraviolet also causes some fabrics and materials such as those used in clothes, furniture, and car interiors to fade and become brittle.

Light From the Sun

Herschel's and Ritter's experiments showed that sunlight contains more energy than "meets the eye." As shown in the diagram below, most of the energy that reaches Earth is in the form of infrared, visible, and ultraviolet light waves. The diagram also shows that much of the energy given off by the sun never reaches Earth's surface. The gases of Earth's atmosphere reflect and absorb some of the energy. The atmosphere acts as a shield that protects all living things from most of the very dangerous short-wavelength, high-energy ultraviolet, X-rays, and gamma rays. Although ultraviolet has less energy than other short-wavelength waves (like gamma rays and X-rays), they pose more of a hazard to living things because more ultraviolet reaches Earth's surface. If Earth did not have a thick atmosphere, much more electromagnetic energy would reach Earth's surface, causing more harm to living things.

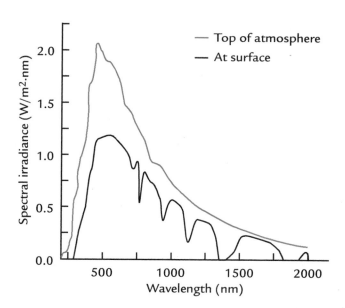

Amount of energy from the sun reaching earth

The Electromagnetic Spectrum

In addition to infrared, visible, and ultraviolet, the sun emits other kinds of invisible electromagnetic energies. They include radio waves, microwaves, X-rays, and gamma rays. Together, the continuous range of all possible electromagnetic wavelengths makes up the **electromagnetic spectrum** shown to the right.

Although ranges of wavelengths in the electromagnetic spectrum are given specific names, such as radio, visible, and X-rays, the categories overlap. This is because it is often hard to define where one group of wavelengths ends and the next one begins. In fact, all electromagnetic energy has certain common traits. For example, all electromagnetic waves can travel through a medium or through a vacuum. They can all be reflected, absorbed, and transmitted through various materials. The degree to which each type will reflect, absorb, or transmit depends on the wavelength of the wave and the surface or material it hits. For example, electromagnetic energy with the wavelength of microwaves is readily absorbed by water but not by other common materials. This is why water (and foods containing water) heat up more quickly in a microwave than in a conventional oven.

Although electromagnetic waves have many things in common, there is a huge difference in wavelength from one end of the spectrum to the other. Wavelengths range from less than one trillionth of a meter for gamma rays to 100 km and more for radio waves. Each range has some unique characteristics. For the same intensity, electromagnetic waves with shorter wavelengths (higher frequencies) carry more energy than those with longer wavelengths (lower frequencies). This is why waves from ultraviolet to gamma rays can penetrate living cells and damage them. Longer wavelengths of energy, like those in the radio range, can be generated or received by antennae. Human eyes can only detect a very small range of wavelengths from 380–750 nanometers (nm). One nanometer is equal to one billionth of a meter.

Electromagnetic Energy and Sound Energy

In many ways, visible light waves, and all the other types of electromagnetic waves, behave much like sound waves. However, there are some very significant differences. Sound requires a medium through which it is transmitted, but electromagnetic energy does

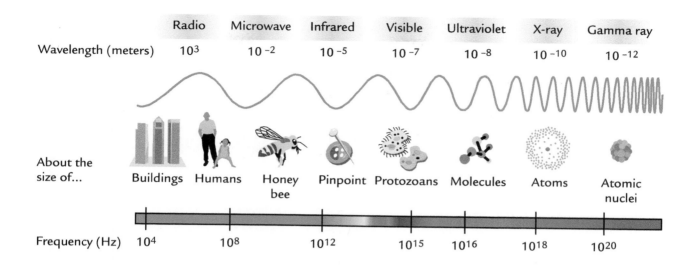

	Radio	Microwave	Infrared	Visible	Ultraviolet	X-ray	Gamma ray
Wavelength (meters)	10^3	10^{-2}	10^{-5}	10^{-7}	10^{-8}	10^{-10}	10^{-12}
About the size of...	Buildings Humans	Honey bee	Pinpoint	Protozoans	Molecules	Atoms	Atomic nuclei
Frequency (Hz)	10^4	10^8	10^{12}	10^{15}	10^{16}	10^{18}	10^{20}

The electromagnetic spectrum

not and can, therefore, be transmitted through a vacuum. This is why sunlight is able to travel from the sun to Earth and through the void of space. Because light waves do not require the presence of atoms or molecules to be transmitted, they are not considered to be mechanical waves. Light is a transverse wave that carries electromagnetic energy. Electromagnetic waves also travel much faster than sound waves, as shown in the tables below.

Speed of Light	
MEDIUM	**SPEED (m/s)**
Diamond	124,000,000
Glass	197,200,000
Plexiglass	198,500,000
Water	224,900,000
Ice	228,800,000
Air	299,700,000
Vacuum	299,800,000

Speed of Sound	
MEDIUM	**SPEED (m/s)**
Vacuum	0
Carbon dioxide (0°C)	258
Air (20°C)	344
Helium (20°C)	927
Water, fresh (20°C)	1,481
Wood	3,500
Aluminum	6,400

Extending Our Senses with Electromagnetic Energy

We use electromagnetic waves in many ways in our daily lives. For example, we use X-rays to scan bones and teeth. Some remote controls send infrared signals to devices, such as TVs. Wireless Internet connections rely on radio or microwaves to send and receive data.

Microwave ovens transmit microwave energy to the water in food, thereby heating it.

Electromagnetic waves allow us to extend our senses. One way is through infrared imaging in night-vision goggles. Night-vision technology lets us see objects by changing the infrared rays given off by objects into an image we can see. Since warm bodies give off infrared energy, a person wearing night-vision goggles can scan an area to see people and other warm-blooded animals in the darkness. Additionally, there are tools that can sense various ranges of electromagnetic energy. For example, astronomers use radio telescopes that detect radio waves. Astronomers use these telescopes to "see" distant objects in the universe.

An astronomer inspects a radio telescope in Germany.

ANALYSIS

1. With what evidence did Herschel support his discovery of infrared energy?

2. With what evidence did Ritter support his discovery of ultra-violet energy?

3. Compare infrared and ultraviolet. In what ways are these two energies similar? In what ways are they different?

4. From the following list, choose the option that describes the fraction of the electromagnetic spectrum that is visible.

    a. more than 1/2

    b. about 1/2

    c. 1/4–1/2

    d. 1/10–1/4

    e. much less than 1/10

Explain your reasoning, citing evidence from this activity.

5. Is it likely that light with frequencies higher than ultraviolet was the main cause of Tía Ana's cataracts? Explain why or why not.

6. Provide an example, not found in the Reading, of a tool that uses electromagnetic waves to help scientists more accurately measure, explore, model, and compute during scientific investigation. Explain how the tool works.

13 *Where Does The Light Go?*

LABORATORY

IN THE PREVIOUS activity, "Selective Transmission," you learned that electromagnetic energy is selectively transmitted by some objects. This means that not all frequencies of light are transmitted through an object when light hits the object's surface. Energy transmission depends on the combination of the wave's wavelength and the properties of the material it hits. Like other activities in this unit, you will use a model to gather evidence on whether electromagnetic energy can also be selectively absorbed and reflected. A **model** is any representation of a system or its components used to help one understand and communicate how the system works.

GUIDING QUESTION

How do different materials absorb or reflect light?

MATERIALS

For each group of four students

    1 UV card
    1 card holder
    3 thermometers
    1 piece of wrinkled aluminum foil
    1 black cloth
    1 dark cloth or paper covering
    1 timer

An Inupiaq guide protects his eyes, left, by wearing glasses that reflect light. The black asphalt, right, absorbs more sunlight than the surrounding land

SAFETY NOTE

Do not look directly into the sun as it can permanently damage your eyes.

PROCEDURE

Part A: Reflection

1. Before going outside, assemble the UV card in the card holder with the card facing down. Cover the assembly with the cloth covering before going outside.

2. Go outside and spread out the black cloth and the piece of wrinkled aluminum foil next to each other in the sunlight.

3. With the dark cloth covering the UV card assembly, place the assembly on the wrinkled aluminum foil and the black cloth so that one side of the UV card is exposed only to the foil while the other side is exposed only to the black cloth, as shown below. Be sure to direct the assembly toward the sun so the assembly does not cast any shadow on the cloth or foil.

4. Expose the setup to sunlight for exactly 20 s. Remove the UV card from the sun and look at the UV-sensitive strip. Compare both sides and record your observations in your science notebook.

5. Place the UV card in a dark place (such as a pocket, where it will reset) or turn the sensitive strip face down.

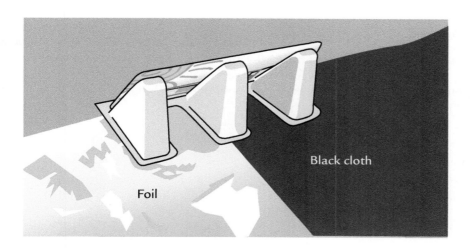

Foil

Black cloth

Part B: Absorption

6. In your science notebook, make a table like the one below.

Temperature Changes

Material	Initial Temperature (°C)	Final Temperature (°C)	Change in Temperature (°C)
Black cloth			
Aluminum foil			
Control			

7. Place the three thermometers next to each other in the shade outside. Wait 1 min, and then record the initial temperatures of each thermometer in your data table.

8. Place one thermometer on top of the aluminum foil and the other on top of the black cloth. Fold the bottom of each material so that it covers the bulb of the thermometer, as shown below. Leave the third thermometer uncovered to serve as a control.

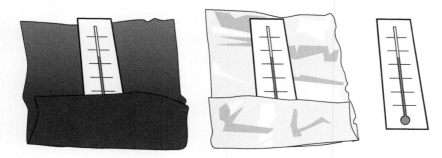

9. Expose all three thermometers to sunlight for 5 min. After 5 min, record the final temperature of each thermometer.

10. Calculate the change in temperature of each thermometer, and record your data in your science notebook.

ANALYSIS

1. Which surface—the black cloth or the aluminum foil—reflected more ultraviolet on the UV card? Cite evidence from this activity to support your answer.

2. Copy the diagrams below.
   a. For each diagram, draw a line that represents how the waves are reflected, absorbed, and/or transmitted through the materials.
   b. For each diagram, explain what you drew.
   c. Use the diagrams to predict if the temperature will increase more in a house with a black roof or in one with a shiny roof.

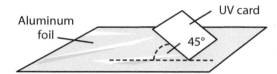

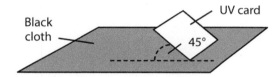

3. In this activity, the black cloth models the dark ground. What could the aluminum foil and the UV card model?

4. Use the model from this activity to explain why there is an increased risk for ultraviolet exposure when playing at the beach or in the snow compared with playing at the park.

5. Provide an example of a material or object that transmits, reflects, and absorbs light simultaneously. Explain how its structure leads to its function.

14 *Blocking Out Ultraviolet*

LABORATORY

IN THIS INVESTIGATION, you will apply what you know about transmission, absorption, and reflection to the use of sunscreens. People often rub sunscreens on their skin to reduce the ultraviolet energy that reaches the skin. The evidence you gather will help you decide if sunscreen absorbs or reflects the electromagnetic energy that is not transmitted.

GUIDING QUESTION

How is sunscreen different from other kinds of lotion?

MATERIALS

For each group of four students

    1 30-mL bottle of moisturizing lotion
    1 30-mL bottle of SPF 30 sunscreen

For each pair of students

    1 UV card
    1 UV card holder
    1 piece of clear plastic
    2 Phospho-boxes
    1 paper towel
    1 timer

SAFETY NOTE

Do not look directly into the sun as it can permanently damage your eyes.

PROCEDURE

Part A: Ultraviolet Transmission

1. Position the clear plastic so that it covers one half of the ultraviolet-sensing strip on the UV card.

2. Expose the UV card to the sun for 20 s. Observe the UV card level of the two sides of the sensing strip, and record your results.

3. To reset the sensing strip, place the UV card in a dark place (such as a pocket) or turn the sensing strip face down.

4. Spread a thin layer of moisturizing lotion on one half of the clear film and a thin layer of sunscreen on the other half, as shown in the diagram below. Make both layers as close to the same thickness as possible.

    Note: Do NOT put the lotion directly on the UV card as it will damage the sensing strip.

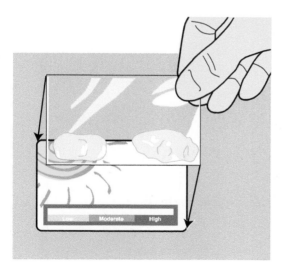

5. Position the plastic over the UV card so that about half of the sensing strip is covered with each kind of lotion.

6. Expose the UV card to the sun for 20 s. Observe the ultraviolet levels of the two sides of the sensing strip, and record your results.

7. When you are finished, clean the lotion off the plastic with the paper towel.

Part B: Ultraviolet Absorption

8. With the equipment assigned to you, design an experiment that will determine whether the sunscreen absorbs or reflects ultraviolet. When designing your experiment, think about the following questions:

   What is the purpose of your experiment?

   What variable are you testing?

   What is your hypothesis?

   What variables will you keep the same?

   What is your control?

   How many trials will you conduct?

   What data will you record?

9. Record your hypothesis and your planned experimental procedure in your science notebook.

10. Make a data table that has space for all the data you need to record during the experiment.

11. Obtain your teacher's approval of your experiment.

12. Conduct your experiment, and record your results.

ANALYSIS

1. What evidence from this investigation indicates that moisturizing lotion has different ingredients than sunscreen lotion?

2. What effect do you think the ingredients in sunscreen lotion have on ultraviolet?

3. Do the results of this experiment allow you to predict the actual results of using sunscreen on your skin? Why or why not?

4. Chlorophyll, a green pigment found in plants and not humans, provides energy to the plant by absorbing light. The graph below shows what wavelengths of visible light that plants absorb.

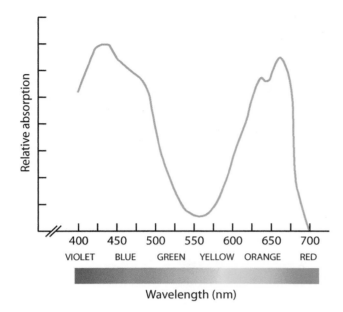

Plant photosynthesis by wavelength

a. Explain what happens to the green light that hits a leaf compared with the red light.

b. Draw a diagram of a leaf with lines showing three different wavelengths of light hitting it. For the wavelengths of 450 nm, 550 nm, and 650 nm, draw what happens to the energy when it is transmitted to the leaf.

EXTENSION

Research the difference between physical and chemical sunscreens. Describe how their structural properties contribute to the function of blocking the sunlight.

WHEN **TÍA ANA** *recovered from her surgery, her sight was much better. José told her about the increased risk of ultraviolet exposure from sunlight. She was impressed that he knew so much about light. José gave her a pair of sunglasses in her favorite color for her birthday. Then he got a pair for himself. Although he still loved spending time outside, José was a little more thoughtful about when and where he was exposed to ultraviolet.*

Although doctors agree that people need vitamin D for many body functions, there is some controversy over whether it is best to obtain it through food, from natural sun exposure, or both. Some doctors support the idea that people should get their vitamin D through eating foods rich in vitamin D, such as seafood and eggs. Other experts recommend limited exposure to sunlight, around 10 minutes a day on trunk and arms without sunscreen, as a way to produce enough vitamin D.

While excessive exposure to ultraviolet increases the risk of health problems, there are trade-offs involved in trying to avoid ultraviolet altogether. In this activity, you will analyze risk factors associated with ultraviolet exposure. Then you will make trade-offs while deciding how to protect yourself from ultraviolet.

GUIDING QUESTION

What personal ultraviolet protection plan fits your risk factors and lifestyle?

MATERIALS

For each student

> 1 Student Sheet 15.1, "Assessing Ultraviolet Risk"

PROCEDURE

Part A: Analyzing Other People's Ultraviolet Exposure

1. Read the ultraviolet exposure risk assessment table below.

Ultraviolet Exposure Risk Assessment: Cataracts and Skin Cancer

Risk Factors	Lower risk	Medium risk	Higher risk
Age at exposure	20 years and over, equal risk		under 20 years
Intensity due to location: latitude	Far from equator	Mid-distance to equator	Close to or on the equator
Intensity due to location: altitude	0 m (sea level)–914 m (3,000 ft)	914 m (3,000 ft)–1,829 m (6,000 ft)	Over 1,829 m (6,000 ft)
Time of day exposure	Before sunup or after sundown	Morning or late afternoon	10 a.m.–2 p.m.
Duration of exposure	Less than 1 h/wk	1–10 h/wk	More than 10 h/wk
Reflectivity	Dirt, grass	Water, sand	Snow
Family history	No history of relatives with skin cancer	A history of relatives who have or have had skin cancer	Close relatives have or have had skin cancer
Skin type: skin cancer	Dark skin	Medium skin	Fair skin
Skin type: cataracts	Equal risk		
Mitigating behavior: hats, sunglasses, sunscreen	Always wear	Sometimes wear	Never wear

2. Read the case studies starting on the next page carefully. Integrate the information from the table and text by completing Student Sheet 15.1, "Assessing Ultraviolet Risk." For each risk factor, assign a value of low, medium, or high risk for each case. If the case study doesn't give you enough information to assign a value, leave the space blank.

3. When you finish all of the cases, go back and check over your ratings.

4. Examine each row of factors, and approximate the cataract and skin cancer risk for each case.

5. Discuss with your class what information is not provided that would be helpful in evaluating risk.

Case Studies

José

José is a 14-year-old, dark-skinned eighth grader who lives near the coast of Southern California. Since he got his dog, Freddie, five years ago, José has spent most mornings and evenings with Freddie at the park. José is amazed that his dog never seems to get tired, even when they have been playing for hours. Every Saturday, José and his friend pack lunches and take them to the beach so they can stay all day. José is concerned about getting too much sun because his great-aunt just had cataract surgery, but he only recently started wearing sunglasses.

Shannon

Shannon is 50 years old and has lived in the mountains of Maine all of her life. She has fair skin and freckles. Because of this, she is careful to wear long sleeves and a hat during the summer when she spends part of the day outside. She also wears sunglasses all summer. As a teenager, Shannon and her twin brother worked at their dad's grocery store after school and spent all of their free time playing basketball or baseball, which she still does on weekends. Last year, her twin had a small dark spot of skin cancer removed from his similarly fair skin.

Leon

Leon, age 68, is very proud of the garden in his backyard. Now that he's retired, he spends several hours each morning tending it. While growing up on the Gulf Coast in Mississippi, he spent afternoons fishing on his dad's small boat. Now on weekends, Leon enjoys taking his own boat to a peaceful cove in the evenings to relax and fish. As a dark-skinned African American, he never thought about protecting himself from the sun. However, recently he has noticed that his vision is a little cloudy. His sister, who lives nearby, says she's having difficulty seeing, too, and just made an appointment to see her doctor.

Sophie

Sophie and her family live in Colorado. She has blond hair, blue eyes, and very light skin. Although Sophie was born with very little hearing, she loves participating in sports, particularly outdoor sports. She spends a lot of time swimming in the summer and skiing in the winter. She enjoys skiing the most, and she spends most winter weekends at her uncle's ski area nearby. He has eye damage from years of skiing, and the weathered skin on his tanned face makes him look older than he is. Sophie always remembers to wear her UV-blocking goggles when she's skiing or sunglasses when just outside in the snow. She also tries to remember sunscreen but tends to forget.

Part B: Your Own Ultraviolet Exposure Risk

6. Create a case study about yourself in your science notebook. Write a paragraph that describes where you live, your activities, and your personal risk factors for cataracts and skin cancer.

7. Add your name at the bottom of the first column on Student Sheet 15.1.

8. Assign ratings to yourself, and approximate your cataract and skin cancer risk.

ANALYSIS

1. In the case studies that you analyzed, who has the greatest risk for
   a. cataracts?
   b. skin cancer?

2. What risk factors are common for both cataracts and skin cancer?

3. Why do you think childhood ultraviolet exposure is considered a bigger risk factor than the same exposure later in life?

4. In the activity, you used a scale of low–medium–high to rate people's risk. Do you believe there can be zero risk of a particular outcome? Why or why not?

5. Use your analysis of your risk from Student Sheet 15.1 to prepare a personal ultraviolet protection plan for yourself. Make a list of all of the things you can do to reduce your ultraviolet exposure while still participating in the outdoor activities that you most enjoy. Then identify any trade-offs that are part of your new strategy.

Waves

UNIT SUMMARY

What is a Wave?

A wave is a disturbance that repeats regularly in space and time and that transmits energy from one place to another with no transfer of matter. If the disturbance is parallel to the direction of wave transmission, the wave is longitudinal. If the disturbance is perpendicular to the direction of wave transmission, the wave is transverse. All longitudinal waves need a medium in which to travel. The material in which the wave energy travels is called the medium. Some transverse waves need a medium where others do not. Electromagnetic waves are an example of a transverse wave that does not need a medium.

Modeling a wave shows a pattern between frequency and wavelength. The frequency is inversely related to the wavelength. Another characteristic of a wave is its amplitude, or its maximum displacement from its state of rest, which is related to the energy the wave being carried.

Characteristics of Sound

A common way of describing sound is with the decibel scale. The decibel (dB) is a unit of measure that indicates the relative intensity of a sound. The decibel scale is used to describe sounds that range from a whisper to explosions. The sound intensity is a measure of how much sound energy passes through a certain area in a certain amount of time as it spreads out from the sound's source.

Sounds can be described by their frequency or pitch. A higher pitched sound has a higher frequency compared with a lower pitched sound. Sound is a longitudinal wave that transfers energy through compressions and rarefactions in the material through which the energy travels. The speed of sound varies with the type of media it travels through. In air, the speed of sound is about 340 m/s.

Hearing Loss

Hearing is a result of sound waves transmitted through the air and into the different parts of the ear. Hearing loss can result from the outer and middle ear inefficiently transferring sound (conductive hearing loss) or when the sound information is not passed to the auditory nerve in the inner ear (sensorineural hearing loss).

Exposure to high-intensity sound or repetitive noises at a specific frequency can damage hearing and lead to sensorineural hearing loss at that frequency.

An audiogram is a graph that shows the results of a hearing test. It shows the sensitivity of a person's hearing for different frequencies. Audiologists use audiograms to evaluate the hearing of an individual and to create a hearing profile that can be programmed into a hearing aid.

Digital Transmission of Waves

Sound can be recorded in its original form (as an analog signal) or converted to a digital signal. Transmitting digital information has emerged as the preferred method for wave transmission in the past 20 years. For digital transmission of sound, the wave is turned into a series of numbers before it is transmitted. When the code arrives at its destination, it is reassembled into the sound wave by a computer. One advantage of digital signals is that digital codes are not subjected to noise interference during transmission the way traditional analog waves are. For storage, digital signals can be infinitely reproduced at the same quality as the original.

Modern hearing aids use a digital technology that can select sounds using a microprocessor. A sophisticated hearing aid can detect and amplify the soft speech while simultaneously cancelling out unwanted background noise.

Characteristics of Light

Light is an example of a transverse wave that can travel through a medium or in a vacuum. Light travels over 800,000 times faster than sound. Like other waves, light can be reflected and refracted. Reflection is the bouncing of a wave off an object. Refraction occurs when a wave passes from one material to another, changing the speed of the wave when it enters the new medium.

When light hits a surface, it can be transmitted, reflected, absorbed, or a combination of all three. Depending on the structure and function of an object, certain frequencies of a wave can be absorbed or reflected while other frequencies are simultaneously transmitted. This is called selective transmission.

Visible light is only a small fraction of the continuous range of all possible electromagnetic waves, called the electromagnetic spectrum.

Other energies that are part of the electromagnetic spectrum include radio, microwaves, infrared, ultraviolet, X-rays, and gamma rays. The sun emits all of these energies, but they are selectively transmitted through the atmosphere. In addition to visible light, some infrared and ultraviolet wavelengths are transmitted to Earth. Ultraviolet carries enough energy to damage the skin and eyes of living organisms, such as humans. This damage can lead to cataracts and skin cancer.

Ultraviolet Exposure

Sunglasses and sunscreen can block ultraviolet waves from damaging eyes and skin respectively. Preventive measures can reduce exposure to this energy. Trade-offs must be made when choosing actions to reduce health risks associated with ultraviolet exposure.

Essential Scientific Terms

absorption	reflection
amplitude	refraction
analog	sound intensity
decibel (dB)	speed of sound
digital	trade-off
electromagnetic spectrum	transmission
evidence	transverse wave
frequency	ultraviolet
infrared	visible light spectrum
longitudinal wave	wave
medium	wavelength

A *Science and Engineering*

THE NATURE OF SCIENCE AND ENGINEERING

F SOMEONE ASKED YOU the question, "What is science?" how would you answer?

You might reply that it is knowledge of such subjects as Biology, Chemistry, Earth Science, and Physics. That would be only partly correct. Although science is certainly related to the accumulation and advancement of knowledge, it is much more than that. Science is a way of exploring and understanding the natural world.

According to the American Association for the Advancement of Science (AAAS), two of the most fundamental aspects of science are that the world is understandable and that scientific ideas are subject to change.

Scientists believe that the world is understandable because things happen in consistent patterns that we can eventually understand through careful study. Observations must be made and data collected for us to discover the patterns that exist in the universe. At times scientists have to invent the instruments that allow them to collect this data. Eventually, they develop theories to explain the observations and patterns. The principles on which a theory is based apply throughout the universe.

When new knowledge becomes available, it is sometimes necessary to change theories. This most often means making small adjustments, but on rare occasions it means completely revising a theory. Although scientists can never be 100% certain about a theory, as knowledge about the universe becomes more sophisticated most theories become more refined and more widely accepted. You will see examples of this process as you study the history of scientists' understanding of such topics as elements and the periodic table, the cellular basis of life, genetics, plate tectonics, the solar system, and the universe in this middle school science program.

While the main goal of science is to understand phenomena, the main goal of engineering is to solve problems. Like science, engineering involves both knowledge and a set of practices common across a range of engineering problems. Just as scientists start by asking questions, engineers start by defining problems. Just as scientists search for explanations for phenomena, engineers search for solutions to problems.

Science and engineering often build on each other. For example, scientists use instruments developed by engineers to study the natural world. And engineers use scientific principles when designing solutions to problems.

Scientific Inquiry

Inquiry is at the heart of science, and an important component of inquiry is scientific investigation, including experimentation. Although scientists do not necessarily follow a series of fixed steps when conducting investigations, they share common understandings about the characteristics of a scientifically valid investigation. For example, scientists obtain evidence from observations and measurements. They repeat and confirm observations and ask other scientists to review their results. It is important for scientists to avoid bias in designing, conducting, and reporting their investigations and to have other unbiased scientists duplicate their results. Some types of investigations allow scientists to set up controls and vary just one condition at a time. They formulate and test hypotheses, sometimes collecting data that lead them to develop theories.

When scientists develop theories they are constructing models and explanations of the patterns and relationships they observe in natural phenomena. These explanations must be logically consistent with the evidence they have gathered and with evidence other scientists have gathered. Hypotheses and theories allow scientists to make predictions. If testing turns out to not support a prediction, scientists may have to look at revising the hypothesis or theory on which the prediction was based.

Engineering Design

An engineer uses science and technology to build a product or design a process that solves a problem or makes the world better. Engineering design refers to the process engineers use to design, test, and improve solutions to problems. Like scientists, engineers design investigations to test their ideas, use mathematics, analyze their data, and develop models.

Since most solutions in the real world are not perfect, engineers work to develop the best solutions they can, while balancing such factors as the function, cost, safety, and usability of their solutions. The factors engineers identify as important for solutions to a problem are called criteria and constraints. Most engineering solutions have one or more trade-offs—desired features that must be given up in order to gain other more desirable features.

References

American Association for the Advancement of Science (AAAS). (1990). Project 2061: Science for all Americans. New York: Oxford University Press.

National Research Council. (2012). *A Framework for K–12 Science Education: Practices, Crosscutting Concepts, and Core Ideas.* Committee on a Conceptual Framework for New K–12 Science Education Standards. Board on Science Education, Division of Behavioral and Social Sciences and Education. Washington, DC: The National Academies Press.

B Science Safety

SCIENCE SAFETY GUIDELINES

YOU ARE RESPONSIBLE FOR your own safety and for the safety of others. Be sure you understand the following guidelines and follow your teacher's instructions for all laboratory and field activities.

Before the Investigation

- Listen carefully to your teacher's instructions, and follow any steps recommended when preparing for the activity.

- Know the location and proper use of emergency safety equipment, such as the safety eye-and-face wash, fire blanket, and fire extinguisher.

- Know the location of exits and the procedures for an emergency.

- Dress appropriately for lab work. Tie back long hair and avoid wearing dangling or bulky jewelry or clothing. Do not wear open-toed shoes. Avoid wearing synthetic fingernails—they are a fire hazard and can tear protective gloves.

- Tell your teacher if you wear contact lenses, have allergies to latex, food, or other items, or have any medical condition that may affect your ability to perform the lab safely.

- Make sure the worksurface and floor in your work area are clear of books, backpacks, purses, or other unnecessary materials.

- Ask questions if you do not understand the procedure or safety recommendations for an activity.

- Review, understand, and sign the Safety Agreement, and obtain the signature of a parent or guardian.

During the Investigation

- Carefully read and follow the activity procedure and safety recommendations.

- Follow any additional written and spoken instructions provided by your teacher.

- Use only those activities and materials approved by your teacher and needed for the investigation.

- Don't eat, drink, chew gum, or apply cosmetics in the lab area.

- Wear personal protective equipment (chemical splash goggles, lab aprons, and protective gloves) appropriate for the activity.

- Do not wear contact lenses when using chemicals. If you doctor says you must wear them, notify your teacher before conducting any activity that uses chemicals.

- Read all labels on chemicals, and be sure you are using the correct chemical.

- Keep chemical containers closed when not in use.

- Do not touch, taste, or smell any chemical unless you are instructed to do so by your teacher.

- Mix chemicals only as directed.

- Use caution when working with hot plates, hot liquids, electrical equipment, and glassware.

- Follow all directions when working with live organisms or microbial cultures.

- Be mature and cautions, and don't engage in horseplay.

- Report any unsafe situations, accidents, or chemical spills to your teacher immediately.

- If you spill chemicals on your skin, wash it for 15 minutes with large amounts of water. Remove any contaminated clothing and continue to rinse. Ask your teacher if you should take other steps, including seeking medical attention.

- Respect and take care of all equipment.

After the Investigation

- Dispose of all chemical and biological materials as instructed by your teacher.

- Clean up your work area, replace bottle caps securely, and follow any special instructions.

- Return equipment to its proper location.

- Wash your hands with soap and warm water for at least 20 seconds after any laboratory activity, even if you wore protective gloves.

Your teacher will give you an agreement similar to the one below to sign.

Science Safety Agreements

STUDENT

I, _____, have read the attached Science Safety Guidelines for students and have discussed them in my classroom. I understand my responsibilities for maintaining safety in the science classroom. I agree to follow these guidelines and any additional rules provided by the school district or my teacher.

Student Signature_____

Date_____

PARENT OR GUARDIAN

Please review with your student the attached Science Safety Guidelines, which include the safety responsibilities and expectations for all students. It is important that all students follow these guidelines in order to protect themselves, their class-mates, and their teachers from accidents. Please contact the school if you have any questions about these guidelines.

I, _____, have read the attached guidelines and discussed them with my child. I understand that my student is responsible for following these guidelines and any additional instructions at all times.

Parent or Guardian Signature_____

Date_____

C Science Skills

N THE FOLLOWING PAGES are instructions you can use to review the following important science skills:

- Reading a Graduated Cylinder

- Using a Dropper Bottle

- Bar Graphing Checklist

- Scatterplot and Line Graphing Checklist

- Interpreting Graphs

- Elements of Good Experimental Design

- Using Microscopes

READING A GRADUATED CYLINDER

A graduated cylinder measures the volume of a liquid, usually in milliliters (mL). To measure correctly with a graduated cylinder:

1. Determine what measurement each unmarked line on the graduated cylinder represents.

2. Set the graduated cylinder on a flat surface and pour in the liquid to be measured.

3. Bring your eyes to the level of the fluid's surface. (You will need to bend down!)

4. Read the graduated cylinder at the lowest point of the liquid's curve (called the meniscus).

5. If the curve falls between marks, estimate the volume to the closest mL.

The example below shows a plastic graduated cylinder that contains 42 mL of liquid.

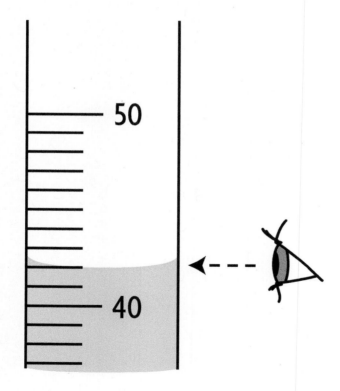

USING A DROPPER BOTTLE

Incorrect

Holding the dropper bottle at an angle gives drops that vary in size.

Correct

Holding the dropper bottle vertically gives drops that are more consistent in size.

BAR GRAPHING CHECKLIST

Sample Graph

Follow the instructions below to make a sample bar graph.

☐ Start with a table of data. This table represents the amount of Chemical A that the Acme Company used each year from 2011 to 2015.

Year	Chemical A used (kg)
2011	100
2012	80
2013	110
2014	90
2015	105

☐ Determine whether a bar graph is the best way to represent the data.

☐ If so, draw the axes. Label them with the names and units of the data.

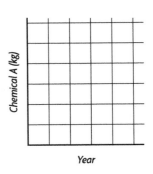

Year

Year axis: 1 block = 1 year

Chemical A axis: 1 block = 20 kilograms

☐ Decide on a scale for each axis. Be sure there is enough space for all the data, but that it's not too crowded.

☐ Mark intervals on the graph, and label them clearly.

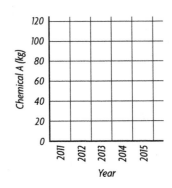

BAR GRAPHING CHECKLIST (continued)

☐ Plot your data on the graph.

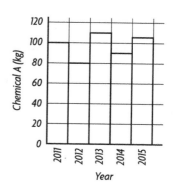

☐ Fill in the bars.

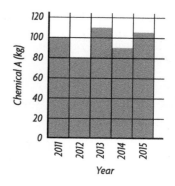

☐ Title your graph. The title should describe what the graph shows.

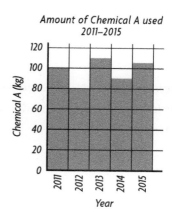

SCATTERPLOT AND LINE GRAPHING CHECKLIST

Sample Graph

Follow the instructions below to make a sample line graph.

☐ Start with a table of data.

MOTION OF A BALL

Time (minutes)	Distance (meters)
0	0
1	5
2	9
3	16
4	20
5	27

☐ Determine whether a line graph or a scatterplot is the best way to represent the data.

LINE GRAPH

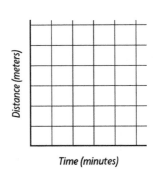

Time axis: 1 block = 1 minute

Distance axis: 1 block = 5 meters

☐ Draw the axes. Label them with the names and units of the data.

☐ Decide on a scale for each axis. Be sure there is enough space for all the data, but that it's not too crowded.

☐ Draw intervals on the graph, and label them clearly.

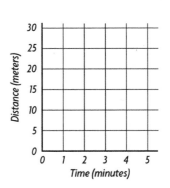

SCATTERPLOT AND LINE GRAPHING CHECKLIST (continued)

☐ Plot your data on the graph.

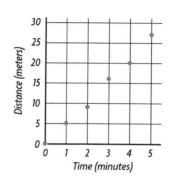

☐ For a scatterplot, leave the points unconnected.

For a line graph, draw a smooth line or curve that follows the pattern indicated by the position of the points.

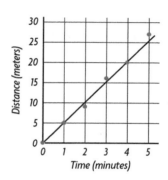

☐ Title your graph. The title should describe what the graph shows.

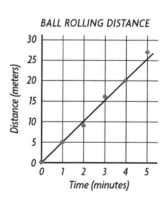

☐ If more than one data set has been plotted, include a key

● = large ball
○ = small ball

INTERPRETING GRAPHS

Determine the path that describes the data

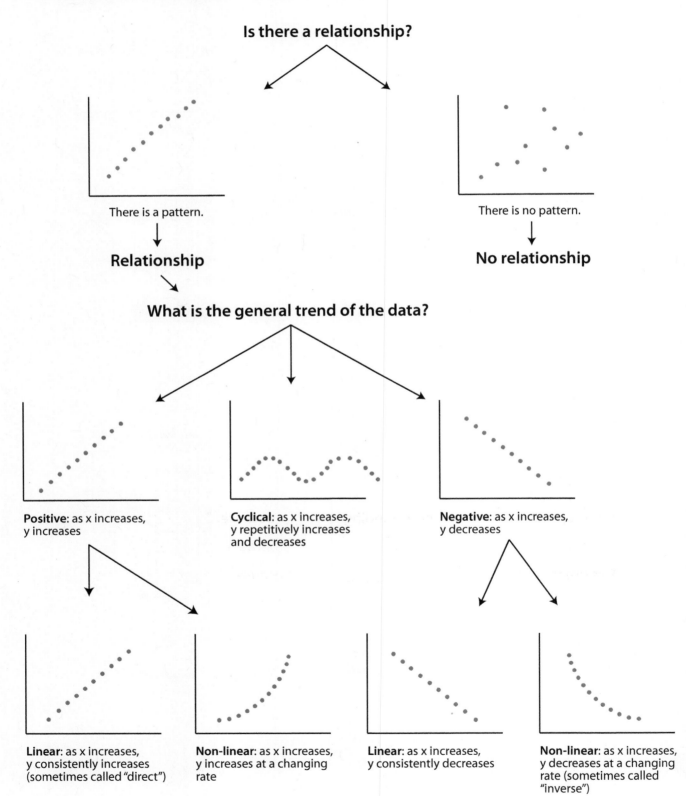

Is there a relationship?

There is a pattern.

Relationship

There is no pattern.

No relationship

What is the general trend of the data?

Positive: as x increases, y increases

Cyclical: as x increases, y repetitively increases and decreases

Negative: as x increases, y decreases

Linear: as x increases, y consistently increases (sometimes called "direct")

Non-linear: as x increases, y increases at a changing rate

Linear: as x increases, y consistently decreases

Non-linear: as x increases, y decreases at a changing rate (sometimes called "inverse")

INTERPRETING GRAPHS (continued)

Define the components of the graph.

Things you can say:

"The title of the graph is..."

"The independent variable in this graph is..."

"The dependent variable in this graph is..."

"_____ is measured in _____"

Create a description of what the graph reveals.

Things you can say:

"This graph shows..."

"As the _____ increases, the..."

"The _____ has the highest..."

"_____ is different from _____ because..."

"The_____ peaked at..."

"The rate of _____ increased from..."

Describe how the graph relates to the topic.

Things you can say...

"This graph is important to understanding _____because..."

"This graph supports the claim that _____ because...."

"This graph refutes the claim that _____ because...."

ELEMENTS OF GOOD EXPERIMENTAL DESIGN

An experiment that is well designed:

- builds on previous research.

- is based on a question, observation, or hypothesis.

- describes all steps in a procedure clearly and completely.

- includes a control for comparison.

- keeps all variables—except the one being tested—the same.

- describes all data to be collected.

- includes precise measurements and all records of data collected during experiment.

- may require multiple trials.

- can be reproduced by other investigators.

- respects human and animal subjects.

Note: Elements may vary, depending on the problem being studied.

USING MICROSCOPES

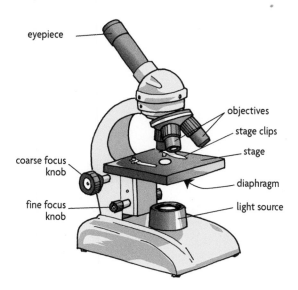

eyepiece

objectives

stage clips

stage

coarse focus
knob

diaphragm

fine focus
knob

light source

Focusing a Microscope

Be sure that your microscope is set on the lowest power before placing your slide onto the microscope stage. Place the slide on the microscope stage. Center the slide so that the sample is directly over the light opening, and adjust the microscope settings as necessary. If the microscope has stage clips, secure the slide in position so that it does not move.

- Observe the sample. Focus first with the coarse-focus knob, and then adjust the fine-focus knob.

- After switching to a higher power magnification, be careful to adjust the focus with the fine-focus knob only.

- Return to low power before removing the slide from the microscope stage.

Safety

Always carry a microscope properly with both hands—one hand underneath and one holding the microscope arm. When you are working with live organisms, be sure to wash your hands thoroughly after you finish the laboratory.

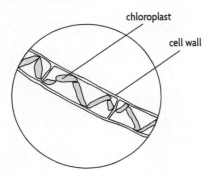

Spirogyra (algae) x 400

chloroplast

cell wall

Some Tips for Better Drawings:

- Use a sharp pencil and have a good eraser available.

- Try to relax your eyes when looking through the eyepiece. You can cover one eye or learn to look with both eyes open. Try not to squint.

- Look through your microscope at the same time as you do your drawing. Look through the microscope more than you look at your paper.

- Don't draw every small thing on your slide. Just concentrate on one or two of the most common or interesting things.

- You can draw things larger than you actually see them. This helps you show all of the details you see.

- Keep written words outside the circle.

- Use a ruler to draw the lines for your labels. Keep lines parallel—do not cross one line over another.

- Remember to record the level of magnification next to your drawing.

The International System of Units

MEASUREMENTS THAT APPEAR IN this program are expressed in metric units from the International System of Units, otherwise known as SI units (from Système Internationale d'Unités), which was established by international agreement. Virtually all countries in the world mandate use of the metric system exclusively. The United States does not use the metric system for many measurements, although it has been the standard for the scientific community in the United States for more than 200 years. A U.S. government effort to convert from the United States customary system to metric measurements in all realms of life has yet to extend far beyond governmental agencies, the military, and some industries.

The reason that many countries have replaced their traditional measurement systems with the metric system is its ease of use and to improve international trade. There are far fewer units to understand in comparison to the system commonly used in the United States. The metric system has only one base unit for each quantity and larger or smaller units are expressed by adding a prefix. The table below shows the base units in the International System of Units.

Quantity	Base unit
Length	meter (m)
Mass	kilogram (kg)
Time	second (s)
Temperature	kelvin (K)
Electric current	ampere (A)
Luminous intensity	candela (cd)
Mole	mole (mol)

Other international units appearing in *Science Grade 7* are shown in the table below.

Quantity	Unit	Common example
Temperature	Celsius (°C)	Room temperature is about 20° Celsius
Volume	liter (l)	A large soda bottle contains 2 liters.
Mass	gram (g)	A dollar bill has the mass of about 1 gram.
Wavelength	nanometer (nm)	Visible light is in the range of 400 to 780 nanometers

The International System's prefixes change the magnitude of the units by factors of 1,000. Prefixes indicate which multiple of a thousand is applied. For example, the prefix kilo- means 1,000. Therefore, a kilometer is 1,000 meters and a kilogram is 1,000 grams. To convert a quantity from one unit to another in the metric system, the quantity needs only to be multiplied or divided by multiples of 1,000. The chart below shows the prefixes for the metric system in relation to the base units. Note: Although it is not a multiple of 1,000 the prefix *centi-* is commonly used, for example, in the unit centimeter. Centi- represents a factor of one 100th.

Metric prefix	Factor	Factor (numerical)
giga (G)	one billion	1,000,000,000
mega (M)	one million	1,000,000
kilo (k)	one thousand	1,000
<UNIT>	one	1
milli (m)	one one-thousandth	1/1,000
micro (μ)	one one-millionth	1/1,000,000
nano (n)	one one-billionth	1/1,000,000,000

E Literacy Strategies

IN THE FOLLOWING PAGES are templates or instructions for some of the literacy strategies that are used throughout this book. Use them for reference or to copy into your science notebook.

- Oral Presentations

- Reading Scientific Procedures

- Keeping a Science Notebook

- Writing a Formal Investigation Report

- Instructions for Constructing a Concept Map

- Developing Communication Skills

ORAL PRESENTATIONS

- Your presentation time is short. Focus your presentation on the most important ideas you need to communicate.

- Communicate clearly by planning your words in advance. When speaking, talk slowly and loudly, and look at your audience.

- Group members should ask for and give each other support if they need help expressing a key word or concept.

- Include graphs and maps when possible. Make sure the type or handwriting and the images are large enough for everyone in the audience to see them.

- While you have your own opinions on a topic, it is important that you present unbiased and complete information. Your audience can then make their own conclusions.

- All the members of a group must participate.

- Since any group member may be asked to answer questions from the class, all group members should fully understand the presentation.

- In a group presentation, you could all play the role of different experts when presenting your information. The class would represent the community members who might be making a decision on the issue.

READING SCIENTIFIC PROCEDURES

The purpose of reading a scientific procedure is to find out exactly what to do, when to do it and with what materials, in order to complete all the steps of an investigation.

If you read a step and are not sure what to do, try these strategies:

- Re-read the previous step.

- Re-read the step that confuses you. Sometimes re-reading clarifies the information.

- Ask your partner if he or she understands what the step says to do.

- Ask your partner if there are words you don't understand.

- Ask your partner to explain what the step says to do.

- Ask your partner to read the step aloud as you listen and try to do what your partner is describing.

- Re-read the purpose (Challenge) of the investigation.

- Try to say the purpose of the step out loud in your own words.

- Look at the clues in the pictures of the activity.

- Peek at other groups and listen to see if they are doing the step that confuses you.

- Tell your teacher exactly what you are confused about and why it doesn't make sense.

KEEPING A SCIENCE NOTEBOOK

- Write in blue or black ink.

- Cross out mistakes or changes with a single line. Do not erase or use correction fluid.

- Write neatly.

- Record the date of each entry.

- For each new investigation, write down your:

  Title:

  Purpose:
  Re-write the Challenge question in your own words.
  Hint: What are you going to do? Why are you going to do it?

  Materials:
  Place a "√" here after you have collected the necessary materials.

  Procedure:
  Write down whether you understand the procedure.

  Data:
  Record observations, measurements, and other lab work.
  Include data tables, charts, diagrams, and/or graphs when needed.
  Be sure to label your work clearly.

- Sometimes, you may want to:

  Make inferences or draw conclusions based on the data.
  I think my results mean …
  I think that this happened because …

  Reflect on how the activity worked in your group.
  This is what went well . . This is what did not go well …
  If I could do this activity again, I would …

  Think about what questions you still have.
  I wonder if …
  I'm not sure about …

  Keep track of new vocabulary and ideas.
  A key word I learned is …
  I would like to find out what happens when …
  One interesting thing to do would be to …

Name _____ Date _____

KEEPING A SCIENCE NOTEBOOK (continued)

The following is a guide to help you conduct investigations. However, depending on the investigation, you may not always use all of steps below or use them in the same order each time.

Title: Choose a title that describes the investigation.

Purpose: What am I looking for? Write what you are trying to find out in the form of a question.

Background: What do I know about the topic? Write a summary of background information you have on the topic that led to the purpose for the investigation.

Hypothesis: Write a statement about what you predict you will see as data in the experiment to answer the question in the "Purpose" and why you are making that prediction.

Experimental Design: How will you answer the question?

Describe the methods you will use (what you will do) to answer the question.

Use short numbered steps that are easy to follow in the lab.

Make a list of the materials you will use to answer the question.

Outline the variables:

- Independent variable (what is being changed)
- Dependent variable (what is being measured)
- Control (what will be used as baseline comparison

Data: What did you find?

Record observations and measurements.

Use a data table where appropriate to organize the data.

Don't forget to include proper units and clear labels.

At the end of your investigation:

Make inferences or draw conclusions about the data:

I think my results mean …

I think this happened because …

Think about any errors that occurred during the investigation:

What did not go as planned?

What steps were hard to follow while doing the investigation and why?

Think about questions you still have that could lead to new investigations:

I wonder if …

I'm not sure about …

Keep track of new vocabulary and new ideas that could lead to new investigations

I would like to find out what happens when …

One interesting thing to do would be to …

Reflect on how the activity worked in your group

This is what went well …This is what did not go well …

If I could do this investigation again, I would …

©2017 The Regents of the University of California

WRITING A FORMAL INVESTIGATION REPORT (continued)

Use the information from your science notebook to write a formal report on the investigation you performed.

Title:

Choose a title that describes the investigation.

Abstract: What were you looking for in this investigation, and what did you find?

Write a paragraph that summarizes what you already knew about the topic, your purpose, your hypothesis, and your results and conclusions.

Experimental Design:

Describe the materials and investigational methods you used to answer the question.

State what variables you worked with and any controls.

Data: What did you find?

Report observations and measurements. Include an organized data table if appropriate to help someone reviewing your report to easily see the results.

Don't forget to use proper units of measurement and write clear labels for your table columns.

Data Analysis: Represent the data in a way that can be easily interpreted.

Use graphs, diagrams, or charts where appropriate to help a reviewer interpret your data.

Conclusion: What do the data mean?

Summarize the data.

Discuss your conclusion based on the accuracy of your hypothesis and the data you collected.

Discuss any errors that occurred that may have interfered with the results.

Describe any changes that need to be made the next time the investigation is performed.

Describe any new questions to be investigated based on the results of this investigation.

INSTRUCTIONS FOR CONSTRUCTING A CONCEPT MAP

1. Work with your group to create a list of 15–20 words related to the topic.

2. If you are uncertain of the meaning of a word, look it up in the book or your notes or discuss it with your group.

3. Discuss with your group how all of the words on your list are related, and sort your list of words into 3–5 categories based on these relationships.

   Remember to listen to and consider the ideas of other members of your group. If you disagree with others in your group, explain to the rest of the group why you disagree.

4. Identify words that can be used to describe each category.

5. Work with your group to create a concept map on this topic. Follow these steps:

   a. Write the topic in the center of your paper, and circle it.

   b. Place the words describing each category around the topic. Circle each word.

   c. Draw a line between the topic and each category. On each line, explain the relationship between the topic and the category.

   d. Repeat Steps 5b and 5c as you continue to add all of the words on your list to your concept map.

   e. Add lines to connect other related words. Explain the relationship between the words on the line.

6. View the concept maps of other groups. As you look at their concept maps, observe similarities and differences between their maps and yours. Discuss your observations with your group members.

Name _____ Date _____

DEVELOPING COMMUNICATION SKILLS

COMMUNICATION	SENTENCE STARTERS
To better understand	One point that was not clear to me was . . . Are you saying that . . . Can you please clarify . . .
To share an idea	Another idea is to . . . What if we tried . . . I have an idea. We could try . . .
To disagree	I see your point, but what about . . . Another way of looking at it is . . . I'm still not convinced that . . .
To challenge	How did you reach the conclusion that . . . What makes you think that . . . How does it explain . . .
To look for feedback	What would help me improve . . . Does it make sense, what I said about . . .
To provide positive feedback	One strength of your idea is . . . Your idea is good because . . . I have an idea. We coud try . . .
To provide constructive feedback	The argument would be stronger if . . . Another way to do it would be . . . What if you said it like this . . .
To discuss information presented in text and graphics	I'm not sure I completely understand this, but I think it may mean... I know something about this from... A question I have about this is... If we look at the graphic, it shows...

F

Media Literacy

MAGINE YOURSELF READING A magazine. A feature article summarizes recent studies on the effectiveness of vitamin supplements and concludes that taking vitamin pills and liquids is a waste of money. A few pages later, an advertisement from a vitamin company claims that one of its products will protect you from all sorts of diseases. Such wide differences in claims that you will see in the popular media are common, but how can you tell which one is correct? "Media literacy" is the term that encompasses the skills we need to develop to effectively analyze and evaluate the barrage of information we encounter every day. Media literacy also includes the ability to use various media to create and communicate our own messages.

A strong background in the process of science helps you build two important skills of media literacy: being able to identify valid and adequate evidence behind a claim and evaluating if the claim is a logical conclusion based on the evidence. The skills share much in common with the process of scientific inquiry, in which you learn to seek out information, assess the information, and come to a conclusion based on your findings.

Evaluating Media Messages

A "media message" is an electronic, digital, print, audible, or artistic visual message created to transmit information. Media messages can include newspaper articles, political advertisements, speeches, artwork, or even billboards. The following are some of the kinds of questions you might ask as you learn to critically analyze and evaluate messages from various kinds of media. On the next page are three examples of media messages, all related to a common theme. Use these three examples to analyze and evaluate the messages.

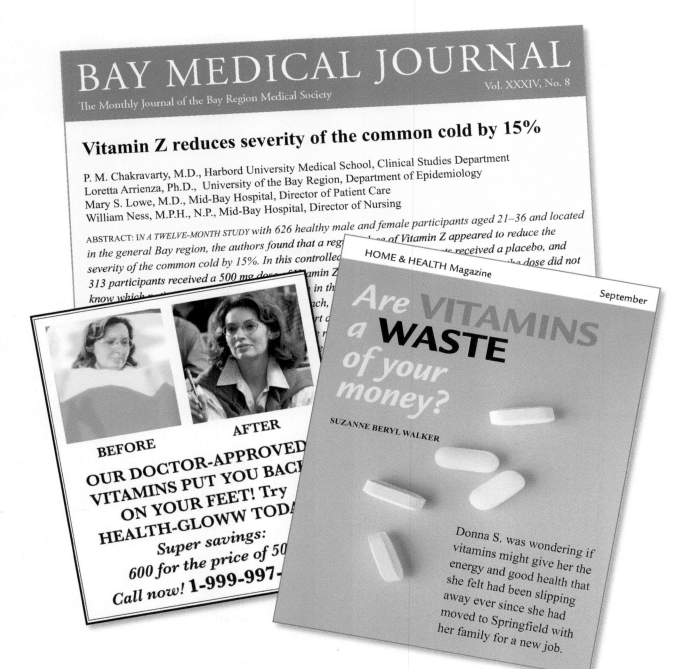

BAY MEDICAL JOURNAL
Vol. XXXIV, No. 8
The Monthly Journal of the Bay Region Medical Society

Vitamin Z reduces severity of the common cold by 15%

P. M. Chakravarty, M.D., Harbord University Medical School, Clinical Studies Department
Loretta Arrienza, Ph.D., University of the Bay Region, Department of Epidemiology
Mary S. Lowe, M.D., Mid-Bay Hospital, Director of Patient Care
William Ness, M.P.H., N.P., Mid-Bay Hospital, Director of Nursing

ABSTRACT: IN A TWELVE-MONTH STUDY with 626 healthy male and female participants aged 21–36 and located in the general Bay region, the authors found that a reg... ...ose of Vitamin Z appeared to reduce the severity of the common cold by 15%. In this controlled... ...s received a placebo, and 313 participants received a 500 mg dose of Vitamin Z... ...he dose did not know which...

BEFORE   AFTER

OUR DOCTOR-APPROVED
VITAMINS PUT YOU BACK
ON YOUR FEET! Try
HEALTH-GLOWW TODA...
Super savings:
600 for the price of 50...
Call now! **1-999-997-...**

HOME & HEALTH Magazine
September

Are VITAMINS a WASTE of your money?
SUZANNE BERYL WALKER

Donna S. was wondering if vitamins might give her the energy and good health that she felt had been slipping away ever since she had moved to Springfield with her family for a new job.

1. **Who created this message?**
   Is this person an expert in the content of the message? What credentials does this person have that would make them an expert in this topic? Does this person have any conflicts of interest that may make him or her biased in any way? Who sponsored (or paid for) the message? Does the source of funding have any conflicts of interest?

2. What creative techniques in the message attract a person's attention?

Are there any sensational or emotional words, images, or sounds that grab the viewer's attention? Do any of these words, images, or sounds try to stir up emotions and influence the viewer's ideas?

3. Does the message cite or mention appropriate sources of factual information?

Does the author cite first-person sources when reporting facts? Are the author's sources from credible organizations?

4. Does the presented evidence completely support the claim?

Might there be other information that could support or discredit the message? Does the author make logical inferences and conclusions from the evidence presented in the article?

5. Who is the target audience of this message?

How is this message directed at this particular audience?

6. Is the message promoting certain values, lifestyles, positions, or ideas either directly or indirectly?

Are there any positions or ideas that are being promoted that are not explicit in the message?

Evaluating Internet Sources

Imagine that you want to search the Internet to find out about the effectiveness of vitamin supplements so that you can come to your own conclusion. When you are searching for information online, a search engine is searching from over one trillion websites.[1] Determining which websites and sources of information are reliable and which are biased is difficult. To make an informed decision about this topic, you will need to identify accurate and unbiased websites. Below is a suggested list of questions that will help you determine if a particular website is an accurate and unbiased source of information.

1. Are the authors' names, contact information, and credentials clearly labeled on the website?

Accurate websites will usually contain information from knowledgeable authors who have their names, credentials, and contact information clearly labeled on the website. Some websites are managed by a collection of people or an organization, and information on the exact author may not be clearly stated. However,

1. Alpert, Jesse & Hajaj, Nissan. (July 25, 2008). We knew the Web was big. . . . *The Official Google Blog. Retrieved August 2010 from* http://googleblog.blogspot.com/2008/07/we-knew-web-was-big.html.

these organizations should state the names, contact information, and credentials somewhere on their website of the people who represent the organization.

2. **Is the information and the website up to date?**

   Some information that you may be seeking needs to be current. For example, if you were looking for the number of cars in the United States, you would want the most recent data. A study conducted in 1982 would not be helpful in this case. When seeking information that needs to be current, determine if the date the article or information was written is clearly indicated on the website so you can be sure you are accessing the most recent information. Credible websites will usually indicate the date the article or information was created or last updated. Also, the person or organization maintaining the website should be regularly updating the website, so that the majority of links to other websites work.

3. **Are sources of information clearly cited?**

   When factual information is stated in a website, is the source clearly cited so you can refer back to it?

4. **Are there links to more resources on this topic?**

   Authoritative websites will often provide links to further information from other sources that support their claim. Authors of websites that contain information that is biased or inaccurate usually do not provide additional information that supports their claims.

5. **What are other people saying about the author or the organization that produced this information?**

   If you come across information from an author or organization that you are unfamiliar with, perform a search for other information about the author or organization. What are experts writing about the author's or organization's other work?

6. **Why is this website on the Internet?**

   Was this information put on the Internet to inform or to persuade people? Is the author selling something? What is the author's motivation for providing this information?

Further Resources

Marlene Thier & Bennett Daviss. (2002). *The New Science Literacy.* Heinemann: Portsmouth, NH.

Center for Media Literacy. http://www.medialit.org.

PBS Teachers. Media literacy. http://www.pbs.org/teachers/media_lit.

G Crosscutting Concepts

PATTERNS	A pattern is a set of repeating things or events. Scientists observe patterns in their data. Patterns lead to questions about relationships and ideas about what causes these relationships.
CAUSE AND EFFECT	Events have causes. If "A" causes "B" to happen, they have a cause-and-effect relationship. A major activity of science is to explain how this happens. Sometime the causes are simple and sometimes they are complex. Sometimes both A and B occur, but one does not cause the other.
SCALE, PROPORTION AND QUANTITY	Scientific phenomena occur at various scales of size, time, and energy. Phenomena observed at one scale may not be observable at another scale. Scientists use proportional relationships to compare measurements of objects and events. They often use mathematical expressions and equations to represent these relationships.
SYSTEM AND SYSTEM MODELS	A system is a group of interacting objects or processes. Describing a system, including its components, interactions and boundaries, and making models of that system helps scientists and engineers understand phenomena and test ideas.
ENERGY AND MATTER	Tracking changes of energy and matter into, out of, and within systems helps scientists understand the systems' possibilities and limitations. Many cause and effect relationships result from changes of energy and matter.
STRUCTURE AND FUNCTION	The structure (shape, composition, construction) of an object or living thing determines many of its properties and functions (what the structure can do).
STABILITY AND CHANGE	For natural and built systems alike, conditions are sometimes stable (the same or within a range), and sometimes they change. Scientists study what conditions lead to either stability or change.

Glossary

advantage A property that, in your opinion, is favorable.

amplitude The maximum displacement of a wave from its state of rest. For a mechanical wave, amplitude can be measured as a distance or a pressure.

analog signal A stream of continuously changing value, such as air pressure, that is sent and received in its original form.

analysis (of experimental results) Making connections between the results of an experiment and the idea or question being investigated.

angle of incidence The angle between the incoming light ray and the normal line when light hits the surface of a different medium.

angle of reflection The angle between the incoming light ray and the normal line when light is reflected off a surface.

angle of refraction The angle between the normal line and the path the light travels in the new medium when light is transmitted from one medium to another.

attenuation The gradual loss of intensity of a wave as it travels.

audiogram A graph that shows the sensitivity of a person's hearing for various frequencies.

compression The region of the wave in which the material through which the wave is transmitted is pressed together. For sound, compressions are regions of high pressure.

controlled variable A variable in an investigation or experiment that is held constant.

correlation (in an experiment) A relationship between one event or action and another. There may or may not be a causal relationship between two correlated events.

critical angle The angle of incidence in a more dense medium that produces a 90-degree angle of refraction in a less dense medium.

data Information gathered from an experiment. First-hand evidence from the five senses or from machines that extend our senses.

decibel (dB) A unit of measure that indicates the relative intensity of a sound.

decibel scale A common way of describing intensity of sound relative to the softest audible sound.

dependent variable The observed phenomenon that is being measured.

digital signal A coded system of 1s and 0s that represents information.

disadvantage A property that, in your opinion, is not favorable.

electromagnetic spectrum The continuous range of all possible electromagnetic waves.

electromagnetic wave A transverse wave that transmits energy across distance as changing electric and magnetic fields.

electromagnetism Magnetism associated with accelerating electrical charges.

electron A negatively charged particle found outside the center or nucleus of an atom.

energy transfer The movement of energy from one object to another.

energy transformation The change of energy from one type to another, such as from potential to kinetic.

error Variations between a measurement and the true value of a quantity.

evidence Information that supports or refutes a claim.

extrapolation Using known data to estimate an answer that lies outside the range of the evidence, such as with a graph. *See also* interpolation.

fluorescence A light source that is produced by using higher energy light waves (ultraviolet) to bombard a material.

fluorescent light A light source that uses a fluorescent bulb.

frequency The number of times a an event repeats in a given time. For sound it is the number of vibrations per second.

function A purpose or function which a particular thing can perform.

gram (g) A unit of mass in the metric system; 1 gram is equal to 1000 milligrams.

hertz (Hz) A unit of measurement for frequency. One hertz is equivalent to one cycle per second. The unit is named after the German physicist Heinrich Hertz (1857-1894).

hypothesis A tentative theory used to explain a set of facts. A hypothesis can lead to further investigation to test whether the hypothesis is valid.

incandescent Light that is produced by a hot object. An incandescent lamp uses a filament that is heated by the flow of an electrical current.

independent variable The controlled variable in an experiment.

infer To conclude by reasoning from known facts. *See* inference.

inference A conclusion based on observations or what is already known. *See* infer.

infrared Electromagnetic radiation that has a wavelength longer than visible light but shorter than microwaves.

interpolation Using known evidence to estimate an answer that falls within the range of the evidence, such as with a graph. *See also* extrapolation.

interpret To explain or give an account of facts with regard to the explainer's conception of what the facts mean.

light A type of kinetic energy that is transferred by the rapid movement of electromagnetic fields.

light absorption The process of light entering an object but not exiting the object as light.

light transmission The process of light passing through a vacuum or a material.

liter (l) A unit of volume in the metric system; 1 liter is equal to 1000 milliliters.

longitudinal wave A wave that transfers energy through compressions and rarefactions in the material through which the energy travels.

mass The amount of matter in an object.

media Plural of medium. *See* medium.

medium The material in which wave energy travels. Mechanical waves, such as sound or seismic waves, move through the ground, water, air, and other materials.

meter (m) A unit of length in the metric system; 1 meter is equal to 100 centimeters.

metric system (SI) The worldwide measuring system used by scientists.

model Any representation of a system or its components used to help one understand and communicate how it works.

noise-induced hearing loss (NIHL) Damage to a person's hearing, either temporarily or permanently, resulting from sound exposure.

opaque A material that is not able to transmit light.

parallel Two lines, planes or surfaces that are aligned such that they do not ever meet.

pattern Something that happens in a repeated and predictable way.

perpendicular A straight line, plane or surface that is at an angle of 90-degrees to another line, plane, or surface.

rarefaction The region of a wave in which the material through which the wave is transmitted is spread apart. For sound, rarefactions are regions of low pressure.

rate A ratio of two different kinds of measurement. *See* speed of sound.

reflection A property of waves wherein the wave bounces off an object.

refraction The redirection of light at the boundary between two transparent materials.

risk assessment The breaking down of various events or actions to see the amount and type of risk involved. Sometimes called "risk analysis" or "risk comparison."

risk management A group or individual's change of behavior, lifestyle, or both to reduce the amount of risk involved in a situation, action, or event.

risk The chance that an action or event could result in something unfavorable happening, such as injury.

sampling rate The number of measurements taken per second.

scientific model, *see* model.

sound A form of energy that is transmitted through vibrations of a medium such as air, water, or solid materials and that can be heard.

sound intensity A measurement of how much sound energy passes through a certain area in a certain amount of time as it spreads out from the source; measured in watts per square meter (W/m^2).

speed of sound The rate at which sound travels through a medium. The distance that the sound travels divided by the time of travel.

structure The way something is formed, built, or organized.

technology The application of science to make practical things for everyday life and for use especially in industrial manufacturing and for commercial purposes.

temperature A measure of the amount of molecular motion, often using the Fahrenheit (° F) or Celsius (° C) scale.

tested variable A variable that is changed in a systematic way in an experiment or investigation in order to determine its effect.

total internal reflection The reflection of light that occurs when the angle of incidence is greater than the critical angle for a pair of media.

trade-off An outcome given up to gain another outcome.

translucent Transmitting light diffusely; semitransparent.

transmission The act of energy passing through a medium or vacuum.

transparent The ability to transmit light clearly so that an object can be distinctly seen through a substance.

transverse wave A wave that consists of vibrations that are perpendicular to the direction that the energy travels.

ultraviolet Electromagnetic radiation that has a wavelength shorter than visible light but longer than x-rays.

variable A changing factor. In an experiment, the variable is what is studied, such as the effect that amplitude has on the energy of a wave.

visible light spectrum The part of the electromagnetic spectrum that is visible to the human eye and is perceived as light; the colored light of a rainbow.

volume The amount of space that an object or substance occupies.

wave A disturbance that repeats regularly in space and time and that transmits energy from one place to another with no transfer of matter.

wave speed The distance traveled by a reference point on a wave, such as a crest, in a given amount of time; usually measured in meters per second.

wavelength The length of one wave cycle.

weight The vertical force exerted by a mass as a result of gravity.

Index

A

AAAS (American Association for the Advancement of Science), 89
absorption of light. *See also* reflection.
    modeling, *72*, 74, *74*
        selective transmission, **61**–63
        ultraviolet light, 78
advantage, **125**
amplitude
    definition, **125**
    modeling, *17*
    and wave energy, 17–18, *17–18*
analog signal
    definition, **125**
    telephone model, 27–30
    transmitting. *See* transmission, analog signal.
analysis (of experimental results), **125**
angle of incidence, **53**, **125**
angle of refraction, **53**, **125**
attenuation
    definition, **34**, **125**
    description, 34–35
    diagram, *35*
audiograms
    definition, *7*, **7**, **125**
    examples, 10–*11*
    of normal hearing, 7, *7*

B

bar graphing, science skills, 100–101, *100–101*
bats, hearing, 19, *19*
blocking ultraviolet light, 76–79
breaking the sound barrier, *14*

C

calorific rays, 65
case studies, personal backgrounds, 82–83. *See also* individual stories.
cassette tapes, *32*

cataract risk assessment, *81*
cause and effect, 123
change, 123
characteristics of waves. *See* properties of waves.
chemical rays, 66
cilia, **16**, *16*
cochlea, 15, **15**, *16*
cochlear implants, 37–38, *37–38*
colors of the rainbow. *See* visible light spectrum.
communication skills, 118
compression
    definition, **125**
    modeling, 9, *9*, **9**
concept maps, constructing, 117
conductive hearing loss, 16
controlled variable, **125**
converting analog to digital, 32–33, *32–33*
correlation, **125**
critical angle, **54**, **125**

D

data, **125**
dB (decibel)
    definition, **4**, **125**
    headphone data, *26*
    of some common sounds, 5
decibel scale, **125**
definition, **127**
dependent variable, **125**
digital signal
    definition, **125**
    telephone model, 27–30
    transmitting. *See* transmission, digital signal.
disadvantage, **125**
dolphins, hearing, 19, *19*
drawing of microscopic views, 108
dropper bottles, science skills, 99, *99*

Credits